Success
Assessment Papers

Maths

10 – 11 years · levels 3 – 5

Paul Broadbent

Sample page

paper number for
quick reference

level showing
attainment target

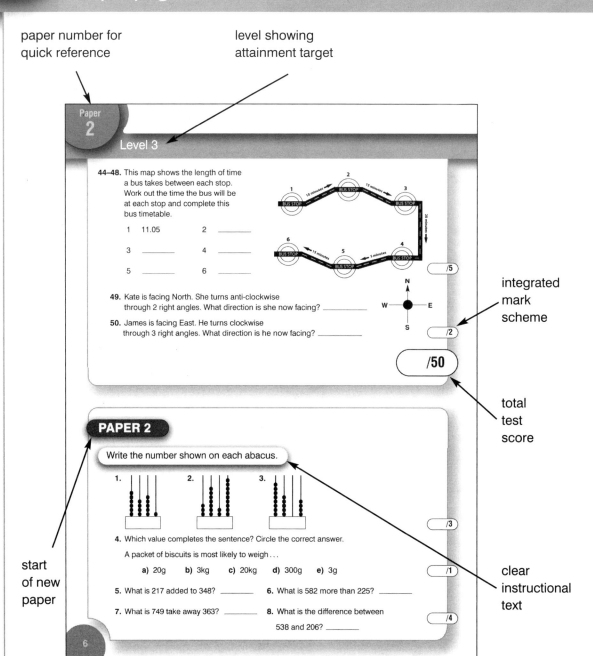

Paper 2

Level 3

44–48. This map shows the length of time a bus takes between each stop. Work out the time the bus will be at each stop and complete this bus timetable.

1   11.05   2   _____

3   _____   4   _____

5   _____   6   _____   /5

49. Kate is facing North. She turns anti-clockwise through 2 right angles. What direction is she now facing? _____

50. James is facing East. He turns clockwise through 3 right angles. What direction is he now facing? _____   /2

integrated
mark
scheme

/50

total
test
score

PAPER 2

Write the number shown on each abacus.

1.   **2.**   **3.**

/3

4. Which value completes the sentence? Circle the correct answer.

A packet of biscuits is most likely to weigh . . .

    a) 20g   **b)** 3kg   **c)** 20kg   **d)** 300g   **e)** 3g   /1

5. What is 217 added to 348? _____   **6.** What is 582 more than 225? _____

7. What is 749 take away 363? _____   **8.** What is the difference between   /4

    538 and 206? _____

start
of new
paper

clear
instructional
text

6

2

Contents

PAPER 1

1. Circle the number that is nearest to 3000.

2980   3020   3018   2986   2899   3011   /1

2–7. Write the next two numbers in each sequence.

| 38 | 49 | 60 | 71 | _____ | _____ |

| 0.8 | 1.7 | 2.6 | 3.5 | _____ | _____ |

| 224 | 112 | 56 | 28 | _____ | _____ | /6

8–10. The digits 1, 2 and 3 are missing. Copy and complete it with the digits in the correct place.

$$
\begin{array}{r}
\square\,7\,\square \\
+\quad 7\ 5\ 8 \\
\hline
9\ \square\ 0 \\
\hline
\end{array}
$$

/3

11–18. Complete this chart.

Shape	Name	Number of faces	Number of vertices	Number of edges
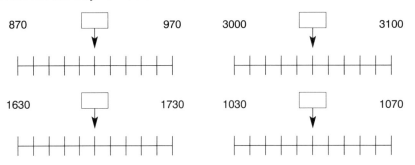	Cuboid			12
		6		
				9

/8

19–22. Write the halfway numbers for each of these number lines.

870   ☐   970   3000   ☐   3100

1630   ☐   1730   1030   ☐   1070

/4

4

23. What is the total weight of these potatoes? _____

24. Three potatoes are removed from the scales and the total weight shown is now 2kg 800g. What is the weight of the three potatoes that have been removed?

_____

/2

25–29. Write these decimals as whole numbers and fractions.

2.8 _____ ⬚/⬚   3.2 _____ ⬚/⬚   15.7 _____ ⬚/⬚   10.6 _____ ⬚/⬚   1.9 _____ ⬚/⬚

30. Cross through the net that will **not** fold up to make a cube?

/5

/1

31–34. Write < or > between these numbers.

7.1 ☐ 7$\frac{7}{10}$ 14.5 ☐ 14$\frac{1}{5}$ 13$\frac{1}{5}$ ☐ 13.4   9$\frac{7}{10}$ ☐ 7$\frac{9}{10}$

/4

35–40. Round these to the nearest 100.

134 _____   591 _____   689 _____

2278 _____   217 _____   1505 _____

/6

Complete these.

41.   938   **42.**   762   **43.**   407
           − 556   − 349   − 288
      _____   _____   _____

      _____   _____   _____

/3

5

44–48. This map shows the length of time a bus takes between each stop. Work out the time the bus will be at each stop and complete this bus timetable.

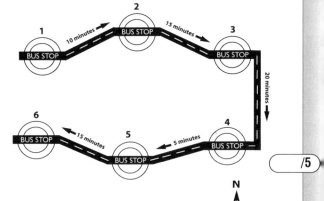

1   11.05

2   _____

3   _____

4   _____

5   _____

6   _____

/5

49. Kate is facing North. She turns anti-clockwise through 2 right angles. What direction is she now facing? _____

50. James is facing East. He turns clockwise through 3 right angles. What direction is he now facing? _____

/2

/50

PAPER 2

Write the number shown on each abacus.

1.

2.

3.

/3

4. Which value completes the sentence? Circle the correct answer.

A packet of biscuits is most likely to weigh...

a) 20g   **b)** 3kg   **c)** 20kg   **d)** 300g   **e)** 3g

/1

5. What is 217 added to 348? _____

6. What is 582 more than 225? _____

7. What is 749 take away 363? _____

8. What is the difference between 538 and 206? _____

/4

What are the numbers shown by each arrow?

9. ☐   4   5   **10.** ☐   **11.** ☐   6

/3

12. Write these temperatures in order from hottest to coldest.

27˚C   –8˚C   14˚C   –15˚C   –11˚C

_____ _____ _____ _____ _____

/1

Use these numbers to answer the problems below.   116   608   780   425

13. Which numbers are exactly divisible by 5? _____

14. Which number is exactly divisible by 3? _____

15. Which of the numbers has a remainder of 1 when the divisor is 4? _____

/3

16–19. Use these signs: = < >. Write the correct signs in each box.

6x4 ☐ 7x3   8x6 ☐ 5x9   6x6 ☐ 9x4   7x5 ☐ 4x8

/4

20–21. Circle the two fractions that are greater than $\frac{1}{2}$.

$\frac{3}{8}$ $\frac{2}{3}$ $\frac{7}{10}$ $\frac{5}{12}$ $\frac{1}{4}$

/2

22. What number is halfway between 36 and 58?

36   ☐   58

/1

Write the next two numbers in each sequence.

23–24.   2206   3206   4206   5206   6206   _____ _____

25–26.   8730   8725   8720   8715   8710   _____ _____

27–28.   134   114   94   74   54   _____ _____

/8

29–30.   578   580   582   584   586   _____ _____

Here are some number cards.

31–32. Use two of the cards to make:

a fraction equal to $\frac{1}{4}$ ☐☐

a fraction which is less than $\frac{1}{4}$ ☐☐

/2

Look at these diagrams.

33. Tick the shape that is a net of a square based pyramid.

34. Draw a circle around the shape that is a net of a triangular prism.

/2

35. A regular hexagon has sides of length 8cm. What is the perimeter of the hexagon?

_____

/1

36. The rule for a number sequence is 'multiply by 2 and subtract 3.' What is the next number in the sequence?

4   5   7   11   _____

/1

37–39. This is a doubling machine. Write the missing numbers in the table.

IN	37		79
OUT		106	

/3

40. Circle three numbers that add together to make a multiple of 5.

9   11   13   15   17   19

/1

41. Write in the missing digits.   26☐ + 8☐ = 350

/1

Write the number that is one more than each of these.

42. 9099 → _____

43. 9909 → _____

44. 9009 → _____

45. 9990 → _____

/4

The digits 1, 2, 3, and 4 are missing from these. Complete them.

46.
$$
\begin{array}{r}
6\ 9\ \boxed{} \\
-\ \boxed{}\ 8\ 1 \\
\hline
4\ 1\ 3 \\
\hline
\end{array}
$$

47.
$$
\begin{array}{r}
7\ 4\ 8 \\
-\ 6\ \boxed{}\ 5 \\
\hline
1\ 3\ \boxed{} \\
\hline
\end{array}
$$

/2

48. If you start at 111 and count on in 5s, will the number 191 be in your counting pattern? _____

/1

49. A clock runs slow and loses 10 minutes every hour. If it is put at the correct time at 5.00, what time will the clock say in 4 hours time? _____

/1

50. A box of four cakes costs £2.72. How much does each cake cost? _____

/1

/50

PAPER 3

Write the missing numbers for each of these.

1. 38.5 x 10 = ☐   **2.** 47.3 x ☐ = 4730   **3.** ☐ ÷ 10 = 34.5

/3

4. A car costs between £4700 and £6200. Circle the prices that the car could cost.

£5008   £6305   £6099   £4588

/1

5. A jug holds $\frac{1}{4}$ litre. A bucket holds 7 litres.
How many full jugs of water are needed to fill the bucket? _____

/1

Circle the largest number and underline the smallest number.

6–7.   0.75   0.9   0.22   0.08   0.83

8–9. $\frac{1}{5}$ $\frac{1}{8}$ $\frac{1}{3}$ $\frac{1}{12}$ $\frac{1}{10}$

/6

10-11. $\frac{3}{10}$ 0.25   0.4 $\frac{7}{10}$ 0.5

9

12. Shade in two more squares to make this shape symmetrical about the mirror line.

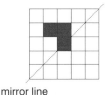

mirror line

/1

> This graph shows the minimum temperature in Nottingham during one week in January.

13. What is the difference between the highest and lowest temperatures during this week? _____

14. On Monday 17th January, the temperature was 5°C less than the previous day. What temperature was it on Monday 17th January? _____

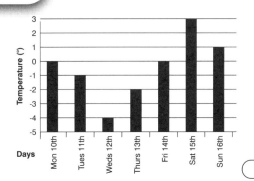

/2

> In a bag there are 6 blue beads, 4 red beads and 2 green beads.

BLUE   RED   GREEN

15. What is the probability of picking a blue bead? Tick the correct answer.

a) 1 in 6 ☐   b) 1 in 12 ☐   c) 1 in 2 ☐   d) 1 in 3 ☐

16. What is the probability of picking a red bead? Tick the correct answer.

a) 1 in 2 ☐   b) 1 in 3 ☐   c) 1 in 4 ☐   d) 1 in 6 ☐

17. What is the probability of picking a green bead? Tick the correct answer.

a) 1 in 12 ☐   b) 1 in 5 ☐   c) 1 in 8 ☐   d) 1 in 6 ☐

/3

18. What is two thousand eight hundred and ninety-nine add one?

Write your answer as a word. _____

/1

> Write in the missing numbers to complete these equivalent fractions.

19. $\frac{2}{3} = \frac{\square}{12}$ **20.** $\frac{4}{5} = \frac{8}{\square}$ **21.** $\frac{3}{5} = \frac{\square}{12}$ **22.** $\frac{3}{4} = \frac{9}{\square}$

/4

23. All of the digits 1 and 3 are missing. Write the digits 1 or 3 in the correct places to complete this addition.

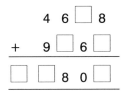

/1

Draw brackets to make each answer 12.

24. 19 – 12 – 5

25. 22 – 5 + 5

26. 6 + 13 – 7

27. 24 – 6 – 6

/4

28–31. Measure each angle using a protractor.

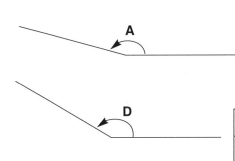
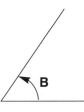
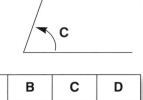

Angle	A	B	C	D
Measured size(°)				

/4

32. A packet of crisps weighs 28g and there are 45 packets in a box. How many grams of crisps are there in a full box? _____

/1

33–36. Write these fractions as decimals

$7\frac{1}{4}$ _____ $4\frac{3}{10}$ _____ $8\frac{7}{100}$ _____ $9\frac{19}{100}$ _____

/4

Complete these.

37. 6708
– 2934
_____

38. 463
× 6
_____

39. 7439
+ 2976
_____

/3

11

Mr. Jones is tiling his kitchen floor.
This is a plan of the floor.

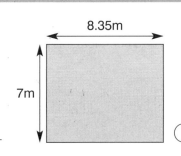

8.35m

7m

40. What is the area of the kitchen floor? _____ m²

41. Floor tiles cost £9.70 for a box of 10. Mr Jones
needs to buy 200 tiles. How much will this cost? _____

/2

42–44. Plot the points (–3, 1), (3, 1) and (3, 4) on the grid.

45. These points are the vertices of a rectangle.
Plot the fourth vertex and draw the rectangle.

46. What are the coordinates of the fourth vertex
of the rectangle? _____

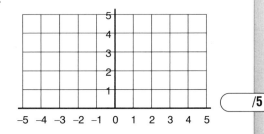

/5

47. Circle the number that is nearest to 3.

2.09   2.89   3.1   3.09   2.92

/1

48. Five bars of soap weigh 850g. What is the weight of three bars of soap? _____

/1

49–50. Tick the two cards that show less than $\frac{1}{2}$.

40% $\frac{2}{3}$ 0.6   0.25   55% $\frac{7}{10}$

/2

/50

PAPER 4

1–2. Circle the two numbers that are multiples of 6.   42   28   40   32   54

/2

3. What fraction is shaded?

4–9. Complete this multiplication grid.

x	4	9	
7	28		21
		72	
6	24		18

/1

/6

10–13. Circle the digit in each number that represents the number written in words.

777777 | seven hundred | 333333 | thirty thousand

888888 | eight hundred thousand | 555555 | five thousand   /4

Look at the two numbers. 8.7 4.8

14. What is the difference between them? _____

15. What is the total? _____   /2

Write the missing digits in these.

16. 3 8 4 ☐
     – 1 7 ☐ 2
     ————
     2 ☐ 8 5

17. 7 ☐ 4 3
     – 2 4 8 ☐
     ————
     ☐ 4 5 7   /2

Write pairs of factors for each number.

18. 27 → (__, __) (__, __)

19. 50 → (__, __) (__, __) (__, __)

20. 18 → (__, __) (__, __) (__, __)

21. 54 → (__, __) (__, __) (__, __) (__, __)   /4

22–25. Write the missing numbers going in and out of this function machine.

IN	3	9		
OUT			73	25

/4

26–29. Name these triangles. Then draw lines of symmetry on them.

_____   _____   /4

30. Write these in order, starting with the smallest.

350ml   3.5l   0.5l   1.3l   1500ml   3300ml

_____ _____ _____ _____ _____ _____   /1

31–34. Write these numbers in the correct place on this Carroll diagram.

18   30   12   24

	Multiple of 4	Not a multiple of 4
Factor of 60		
Not a factor of 60		

/4

35–37. Round these numbers to the nearest 100.

4748 →	
12 291 →	
416 037 →	

/3

38. What is 5.09 as a fraction? Circle the correct answer.   **a)** $5\frac{9}{10}$ **b)** $5\frac{9}{100}$ **c)** $5\frac{90}{100}$ /1

Answer these

39.   39.05
         +52.85
       _____

40.   62.54
         − 21.86
       _____

_____   _____   /2

41–48. Complete this chart. Tick to show whether each angle is acute or obtuse, then measure each angle and write the size on the chart.

Angle	A	B	C	D
Acute				
Obtuse				
Measured size(°)				

/8

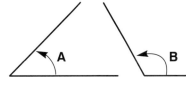
A

B

C

D

49–50. Write the total area of each shape.

a)

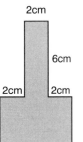

2cm

6cm

2cm   2cm

4cm

area = _____ cm²

b)

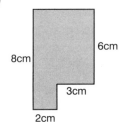

6cm

8cm

3cm

2cm

area = _____ cm²

/2

/50

14

PAPER 5

Hannah buys 9 badges at 49p each and 6 badges at 75p each.

1. How much does she spend on badges in total? _____

2. How much change will she get from £10? _____

3. Three parcels weigh 28kg altogether. Two of the parcels weigh 9.7kg each. What does the third parcel weigh? _____

4–5. On this grid draw a rectangle with an area of 24 squares and a perimeter of 20 squares.

6. What is the perimeter of this room?

_____ m

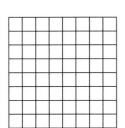

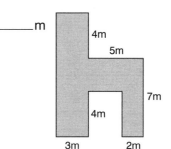

7. What is the missing number? Circle the correct answer. $(19 - 7) + \boxed{} = 18$

    a) 1   **b)** 6   **c)** 8

8. Write these in order, starting with the smallest.

    85kg   8.2kg   850g   8050g   8800g

_____   _____   _____   _____   _____

9–12. Write the missing numbers to complete the fractions.

    $50\% \rightarrow \dfrac{\boxed{}}{2}$ $90\% \rightarrow \dfrac{\boxed{}}{10}$ $60\% \rightarrow \dfrac{\boxed{}}{5}$ $75\% \rightarrow \dfrac{\boxed{}}{4}$

13–18. Join each of these fractions to its correct place on this number line.

$\boxed{\dfrac{3}{4}}$ $\boxed{\dfrac{9}{10}}$ $\boxed{\dfrac{2}{5}}$ $\boxed{\dfrac{1}{4}}$ $\boxed{\dfrac{1}{2}}$ $\boxed{\dfrac{4}{5}}$

0   1

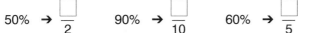

19. What percentage of this grid is dark grey? _____

20. What percentage is light grey? _____

/2

21. Here is a shaded square on a grid. Shade in 3 more squares so that the design is symmetrical in both mirror lines.

/1

22–23. Complete these.

_____ ÷ 10 = 23.45   745 ÷ _____ = 7.45

/2

24. Write these fractions in order, starting with the smallest:

$\frac{3}{4}$ $\frac{1}{3}$ $\frac{1}{4}$ $\frac{1}{12}$ $\frac{2}{3}$

/1

Complete these.

25.
```
    ☐ 9 . 5 3
  + 1 5 . 1 ☐
  _____
    4 ☐ . 6 7
  _____
```

26.
```
    5 ☐ . 0 9
  - 2 7 . ☐ 6
  _____
    2 5 . 1 ☐
  _____
```

/2

27. Circle the division that has a remainder of 1.

281 ÷ 6   347 ÷ 3   237 ÷ 4   695 ÷ 8

/1

Mrs Stevenson set off at 12.00 and travelled 280km in her car in an afternoon. This graph shows her journey.

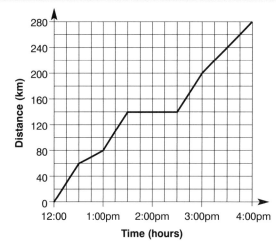

28. How far had she travelled after 30 minutes?

_____

29. At what time had she travelled half the distance? _____

30. What was the average speed of her journey? _____ km/h

/3

31–33. The rule for a number sequence is ▲ = 2■ − 1

Write the missing numbers for the sequence.

■	1	2	3	4	5
▲	1				9

/3

34. Jasmine fills a 3 litre jug with water. She puts 850ml in a cup and pours 1.25 litres into a bowl. How much water remains in the jug? _____

/1

35. Sam buys some sunglasses for £11.54 and a hat for £6.98. What change does he get from £20? _____

/1

36–37. This table shows the number of shirts made in a factory in a month.

	White	Not white
Cotton	2254	3811
Not cotton	5308	6174

How many shirts are white? _____

How many shirts are cotton? _____

/2

38–39. Here are four number cards.
Which two number cards are factors of 42? _____ _____

12   7   4   3

/2

40–41. Look at these diagrams.Put a tick (✓)
if it is the net of a square based pyramid.
Put a cross (✗) if it is not.

/2

42. Five bricks weigh a total of 7500g. What is the weight of eight bricks? _____

/1

43–45. Round these to the nearest whole number.

3.09 → _____   2.73 → _____   11.52 → _____

/3

46–49. Complete this multiplication grid.

x	3	5
46	138	
19		95

/4

50. Which of these fractions is equivalent to 60%? Circle the correct answer.

a) $\frac{2}{3}$ b) $\frac{1}{6}$ c) $\frac{3}{50}$ d) $\frac{3}{5}$

/1

/50

PAPER 6

1. A bag costs £85 and a purse costs £47. Circle the total cost.

   a) £122   **b)** £132   **c)** £112   **d)** £142

   /1

2–5. Write the equivalent lengths.

Length in m and cm	Length in cm
9m 22cm	922cm
_____m _____cm	280cm
3m 25cm	_____cm
_____m _____cm	705cm
6m 9cm	_____cm

   /4

This is a scale drawing of a car.

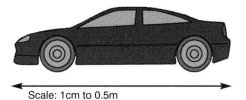

6. What is the length of the scale drawing

   of the car? _____cm

   Scale: 1cm to 0.5m

7. Use the scale to work out the actual length of the car. _____m

   /2

Answer these.

8.   37
     x 41
   _____

   _____

9. 3)‾7‾9‾0‾

   /2

10–13. Write < , > or = to make each statement true.

   $\frac{3}{4}$ ☐ $\frac{2}{3}$ $\frac{5}{6}$ ☐ $\frac{11}{12}$ $\frac{2}{6}$ ☐ $\frac{1}{3}$ $\frac{2}{3}$ ☐ $\frac{7}{12}$

   /4

14. Which of these is a prism? Tick the correct shape.

   a)   **b)**   **c)**

   /1

15–16. Change these 24–hour times into 12–hour times, using a.m. or p.m..

17:30 _____   06:55 _____   /2

17–18. Solve these equations.

$7a = 42$ $a =$ _____ $\frac{y}{8} = 4$ $y =$ _____   /2

19. What is 0.2 x 0.2 x 0.2? Circle the correct answer.

   a) 0.06   **b)** 0.0008   **c)** 0.008   **d)** 0.8   /1

20. I'm thinking of a number. If I add 5 to it and then multiply by 3,
the answer is 36. What number am I thinking of?   _____   /1

21. Underline the prime number.   30   31   32   33   34   35   36   /1

22–23. Write the number shown on each abacus.

     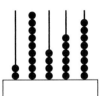

/2

24–32. Complete this table.

	Round to the nearest 100	Round to the nearest 1000	Round to the nearest 10000
29832 →			
60157 →			
25129 →			

/9

33. Two numbers in each sequence have been swapped over. Circle each pair of numbers.

480   478   468   474   472   470   476

3165   3150   3155   3160   3145   3170   3175

/1

34. There are two clocks in a room. One chimes every 5 minutes and the other every 6 minutes.
They chime together at 2 o'clock, what time will it be when they next chime together?

_____   /1

35–38. Write all the even numbers to 30 in the correct sections.

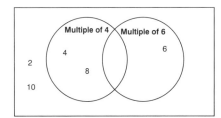

/4

Use these numbers to answer each question.   12 5 8 9

39. Which number is a factor of 64?   _____

40. Which number is a factor of 18?   _____

41. Which two numbers are factors of 36?   _____

42. Which two numbers are factors of 60?   _____

/4

Write **acute**, **obtuse** or **right angle** for each of these angles.

43.

_____

44.

_____

45.

_____

46.

_____

47.

_____

48.

_____

/6

49. Which of these numbers is a common multiple of 3 and 4? Circle the correct answer.

  a) 52   **b)** 64   **c)** 72

/1

50. A farmer is putting a fence around a rectangular field. Two sides of
the field are 3625 m and the other two sides are 1436 m.
What is the total amount of fencing the farmer will need for the field? _____

/1

/50

PAPER 7

1–6. The digits 2, 3, 4, 5, 6 and 7 are missing from these. Complete them.

3 ☐ + ☐ 8 = 8 5   ☐ 2 + 2 ☐ = 8 5   ☐ 6 + ☐ 9 = 8 5   /6

Use these numbers to answer the following:

| 82 | 23 | 48 | 74 | 55 |

7. Which two numbers have a difference of 32? _____

8. Which two numbers have a difference of 8? _____

9. Which two numbers have a difference of 25? _____   /3

Answer these.   **10.**   6728   **11.**   3128   **12.**   1561
                            +2740   +4675   +2918
                            _____   _____   _____

                            _____   _____   _____   /3

Look at these price tags and answer the questions.

Camera
£56.23

Phone
£72.00

Printer
£49.56

Watch
£35.99

13. What is the difference in price between the camera and the watch? _____

14. How much more is it to buy a phone than a printer? _____

15. Mrs Jones has two £20 notes.
How much more does she need to buy the camera? _____   /3

Look at these shapes. Complete each of these statements, using the words **perpendicular** or **parallel**.

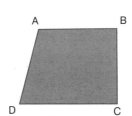

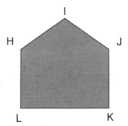

16. AB is _____ to CD.   **17.** AB is _____ to BC.

18. HI is _____ to IJ.   **19.** HL is _____ to JK.

20. JK is _____ to LK.

/5

21–25. Write the decimal number each arrow points to.

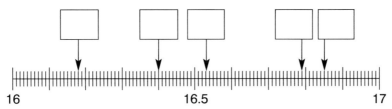

/5

26. Which number from those you have written above rounds to 16.8 to the nearest tenth?

_____

/1

Use a protractor to measure these angles.

27. 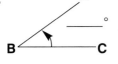   **28.**   **29.**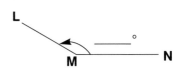

30.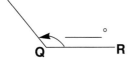

/4

Cross out the odd shape in each set.

31.    **32.**

33.

/3

34–39. Complete these.

55mm = _____ cm   10.64m = _____ cm   810cm = _____ m

9.3km = _____ m   3200m = _____ km   6.25m = _____ cm   /6

40–43. Draw each shape in its correct place on the diagram.

Right angles   No right angles

Quadrilateral

Not a quadrilateral   /4

44–45. Shade each grid to show the percentage given.

40%

80%   /2

46. Use the digits 4, 5 and 6 to make the multiplication with the greatest product. Write the answer.   _____ _____ x _____ = _____   /1

47–48. Write the next number in this sequence.

3   6   10   15   _____

Explain how you worked it out.

/2

There are 140 children in a school. The ratio of girls to boys is 4:3.

49. How many boys are there? _____

50. How many girls are there? _____   /2

/50

PAPER 8

1–2. Write the missing numbers on this number line.

7000   8000

/2

Write the answer for each of these.

3. (18 – 3) + 4 = _____

4. 9 x (8 – 5) = _____

5. (16 + 12) – (3 + 5) = _____

6. (9 x 2) + (4 x 5) = _____

7. (15 – 9) + (13 – 7) = _____

/5

8–9. Round each of these to the nearest whole number of kilograms, then write the approximate total weight for each set.

13.85kg + 12.55kg + 6.53kg   Approx. total weight _____kg

19.09kg + 17.64kg + 8.47kg   Approx. total weight _____kg

/2

Write these times as 24–hour clock times.

10. 11:15am   → : _____

11. 9:55pm   → : _____

12. 4:23pm   → : _____

13. 8:57am   → : _____

/4

This table shows the depths of the deepest oceans and seas in the world. Look at the table and answer these questions.

Ocean/sea	Average depth (metres)
Pacific Ocean	4028m
Indian Ocean	3963m
Atlantic Ocean	3926m
Caribbean Sea	2647m
South China Sea	1652m

14. How much deeper is the Caribbean Sea than the South China Sea?

_____

15. By how many metres is the Pacific Ocean deeper than the Caribbean Sea?

_____

16. What is the difference in depth between the
Atlantic Ocean and the Indian Ocean?   _____

17. Which two oceans or seas have a difference in depth of 102m?

_____

18–21. Write the missing numbers to complete these equivalent fractions.

$\dfrac{1}{3} = \dfrac{\square}{15}$ $\dfrac{2}{5} = \dfrac{8}{\square}$ $\dfrac{3}{10} = \dfrac{\square}{40}$ $\dfrac{3}{8} = \dfrac{9}{\square}$

Use a protractor to measure these angles.

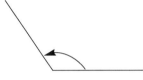

22. _____°

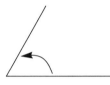

23. _____°

24. _____°

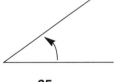

25. _____°

26. _____°

27. Which angles are obtuse?   _____

28. Which angles are acute?   _____

29. Which angle is right-angled?   _____

30. Write these volumes in order starting with the smallest.

Lemonade	Cola	Orange Juice	7.3 litres	Milk
700ml	7500ml	0.75 litres	Pineapple Juice	7 litres
			7 litres	

_____ _____ _____ _____ _____

1

31–40. Write these numbers in the correct part of the Venn diagram.

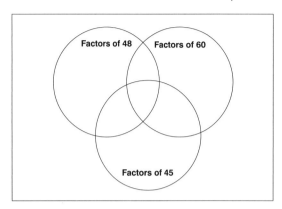

| 12 | 10 | 24 | 16 | 15 |

| 3 | 20 | 9 | 6 | 5 |

/10

Name each shape.

41.   **42.**   **43.**   **44.**

_____ _____ _____ _____

45. Which shape has 5 faces, 8 edges and 5 vertices? _____

46. Which shape has 4 faces, 6 edges and 4 vertices? _____

47. Which shape has 5 faces, 9 edges and 6 vertices? _____

48. Which shape has 6 faces,12 edges and 8 vertices? _____

/8

49. What is the median of this set of numbers? _____

    34   37   31   23   27   37   29

/1

50. What is the mode of this set of numbers? _____

    18   17   19   18   19   13   19

/1

/50

PAPER 9

Write the number shown on each abacus.

1.   **2.**   **3.**

/3

4. Tick the angle that is approximately 100°.

/1

Complete these multiplications.

5.   418
         x 4
         ‾‾‾‾‾

         ‾‾‾‾‾

6.   3273
          x   3
          ‾‾‾‾‾

          ‾‾‾‾‾

/2

7–11. Write the name of each of these shapes from its net.

| square-based pyramid   cuboid   tetrahedron   triangular prism   cube |

a)   **b)**   **c)**   **d)**   **e)**

/5

_____   _____   _____   _____   _____

_____   _____   _____   _____   _____

12–15. Look at this number line and write the decimal number for each arrow.

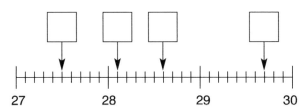

/4

16. What fraction is equivalent to $\frac{1}{3}$? Circle the correct answer.

    a) $\frac{4}{9}$ **b)** $\frac{3}{12}$ **c)** $\frac{5}{15}$ /1

17–25. Complete this table.

	round to the nearest 10	round to the nearest 100	round to the nearest 1000
71653			
20983			
60057			

/9

26–28. What are the halfway numbers for each of these?

    a) 9732 ☐ 9746   **b)** 8117 ☐ 8131   **c)** 5345 ☐ 5365   /3

29–32. Read these and write each as a number.

    four hundred thousand nine hundred and twenty-five   ————————

    one hundred and eighteen thousand and seventy-nine   ————————

    four hundred thousand   ————————

    two hundred and ninety thousand five hundred and ninety-one   ————————   /4

33. Golf balls are sold in packs of six. How many balls will there be in 55 packs? ————   /1

34. A teacher gives a star for every 5 correct answers and a smiley face for every 10 correct answers. Hannah has 50 correct answers. How many times has she had a star and a smiley face at the same time?   ————————   /1

> Count in these steps. Write in the missing numbers.

35. Count back in 10s   ➔   81972   ———— ———— ————   81932

36. Count on in 10s   ➔   5001   ———— ———— ————   5041

37. Count on in 100s   ➔   1872   ———— ———— ————   2272

38. Count back in 100s   ➔   7354   ———— ———— ————   6954   /4

39–41. Write the factors of each of these numbers.

    6 ➔ ————————   27 ➔ ————————   55 ➔ ————————   /3

Two numbers in each sequence have been swapped over.
Write each sequence in the correct order.

42. 480   478   468   474   472   470   476

_____ _____ _____ _____ _____ _____ _____

43. 3165   3150   3155   3160   3145   3170   3175

/2

_____ _____ _____ _____ _____ _____ _____

This function machine multiplies by 40. Complete the table of results for the numbers coming out of the function machine.

44–47.

IN	23	37	51	80
OUT				

/4

48. What is the name for a 7–sided polygon? Circle the correct answer.

a) hexagon   **b)** nonagon   **c)** heptagon

/1

Ahmed plays a computer game each day. He is trying
to reach a total of 10000 points to go on to the next level.
These are his points for the first three days.

49. How many more points did he score
on Wednesday than on Tuesday?   _____

50. How many more points does
he need to reach 10000 points?   _____

Day	Points
Monday	3885
Tuesday	2453
Wednesday	3209

/2

/50

PAPER 10

Write the missing **x10** or **x100** in each of these.

1. 1.5   →   _____   →   15   **2.** 6.29   →   _____   →   629

/4

3. 74.3   →   _____   →   743   **4.** 0.5   →   _____   →   50

29

5–7. What is the area and perimeter of each of these rectangles?

7cm
8cm

4cm
10cm

3cm
10cm

area = _____   area = _____   area = _____

perimeter = _____   perimeter = _____   perimeter = _____   /3

8–13. Look at these shapes and complete the chart by ticking the correct name.

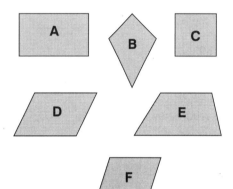

A   B   C   D   E   F

Shape	A	B	C	D	E	F
Square						
Rhombus						
Rectangle						
Parallelogram						
Trapezium						
Kite						

/6

> Complete the equivalent fraction chains.

14. $\dfrac{1}{3} = \dfrac{\Box}{6} = \dfrac{3}{\Box} = \dfrac{\Box}{12} = \dfrac{5}{\Box}$

15. $\dfrac{3}{4} = \dfrac{6}{\Box} = \dfrac{\Box}{12} = \dfrac{12}{\Box} = \dfrac{\Box}{20}$

16. $\dfrac{4}{5} = \dfrac{\Box}{10} = \dfrac{12}{\Box} = \dfrac{\Box}{20} = \dfrac{20}{\Box}$

/3

> Circle the correct answer for each of these.

17. A common multiple of 3 and 5 is: 35   45   55

18. A common multiple of 2 and 3 is: 28   38   48

19. A common multiple of 5 and 6 is: 70   80   90

20. A common multiple of 3 and 10 is: 100   120   160

/4

21. Here is part of a shape. Draw two more lines to make a shape with two lines of symmetry. Use a ruler.

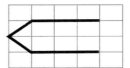

/1

22. A father and his son weigh a total of 87kg.
If the father weighs 68kg 295g, what is the weight of the son? _____

/1

23. What is the value of the bold digit in **8 7**950? Circle the correct answer.

    a) 7   **b)** 7000   **c)** 700

/1

24–27. Answer these.

    38 + 56 = ⬚   54 + 27 = ⬚   34 + 76 = ⬚   78 + 65 = ⬚

/4

28. Which of these numbers is a factor of 54? Circle the correct answer.

    a) 8   **b)** 7   **c)** 4   **d)** 9

/1

> Make different 2-digit numbers with these digits.

    | 5 | 7 | 3 | 9 |

29. What is the largest difference you can make? _____

30. What is the smallest difference you can make? _____

31. Make a difference between the two numbers with an answer as near as possible to 50. _____

/3

32–35. Write these fractions as decimals.

    $6\frac{3}{10}$ _____ $23\frac{9}{10}$ _____ $12\frac{4}{10}$ _____ $18\frac{5}{10}$ _____

/4

36–38. Change these mixed numbers to improper fractions.

    $2\frac{1}{4}$ _____ $4\frac{1}{3}$ _____ $1\frac{5}{8}$ _____

/3

39. Add together 3849 and 5674. _____

40. What is 8029 subtract 3974? _____

41. What is the sum of 2263 and 3815? _____

/4

42. What is the difference between 3983 and 1396. _____

Level 4

43–46. What fraction of each shape is shaded? Write the fraction in its lowest term.

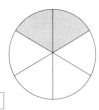 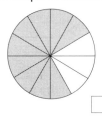 

□/□   □/□   □/□   □/□

/4

47–50. Write in the missing numbers.

(□ x 2) ÷ 3 = 8   42 – (□ x 6) = 30

(8 x 5) + (□ x 3) = 61   (□ x 4) – (54 ÷ 6) = 7

/4

/50

PAPER 11

1–4. Write these as decimals.

$\dfrac{3}{10}$ _____ $\dfrac{8}{10}$ _____ $\dfrac{5}{100}$ _____ $\dfrac{65}{100}$ _____

/4

5. A square has a perimeter of 20cm. What is the length of each side?

a) 4cm   **b)** 10cm   **c)** 5cm

/1

6–9. Complete these.

```
    5  4  9  7          5  2  0  6          2  7  3  4          9  5  4  4
 +  3  1  5  6       -  3  8  4  2       +  5  8  7  8       -  6  2  9  8
 _____         _____         _____         _____

 _____         _____         _____         _____
```

/4

10–17. Write < , > or = to make each sentence true.

1.86m □ 1m 68cm   1m 10cm □ 110cm   472cm □ 2.74m

3m 9cm □ 3.90m   835cm □ 8m 35cm   1.06m □ 160cm

5.81m □ 1m 85cm   46cm □ 0.42m

/8

Look at these shapes. Which shape is each of these describing?

A B C D E

18. 4 right angles and 2 pairs of parallel sides _____

19. 1 right angle, 1 acute angle and 2 obtuse angles _____

20. 2 right angles, an acute angle, an obtuse angle and a pair of parallel lines _____

21. 2 acute angles, 2 obtuse angles and 1 pair of parallel lines _____

22. 2 acute angles, 2 obtuse angles and 2 pairs of parallel lines _____ /5

A shop buys 1035 copies of the Daily Gazette. It sells 748 copies in the morning and 217 copies in the afternoon.

23. How many copies does it sell altogether? _____

24. How many copies does it have left at the end of the day? _____ /2

Add together these prices and write the total amounts.

25. 94p + £15.22 _____

26. £7.40 + 65p _____

27. 89p + £3.06 _____

28. £14.95 + 59p _____ /4

29. How many edges has a pentagonal pyramid got? Circle the correct answer.

   a) 8   **b)** 10   **c)** 12   **d)** 5 /1

30. A farmer has three goats, A, B and C. Each goat is a different weight and is an exact number of kilograms. Goats A and B weigh a total of 20kg. Goats B and C weigh a total of 15kg. Goats A and C weigh a total of 17kg.

What is the weight of each goat?

A = _____   B= _____   C= _____ /1

31. Shade squares on the other side of the lines, so that the pattern has two lines of symmetry.

/1

> Write each set of measures in size order, starting with the smallest.

32. 30cm   3.5cm   3.05m   350cm   _____ _____ _____ _____

33. $\frac{1}{2}$kg   250g   50g   1.2kg   _____ _____ _____ _____

34. 60 litres   6600ml   600ml   6 litres   _____ _____ _____ _____

35. 40m   400cm   4km   400m   _____ _____ _____ _____   /4

> Answer each of these.

36. There are 60 minutes in an hour. How many minutes in 10 hours?   _____

37. 485 people go to a basketball match and tickets cost £10.
How much money in total will there be from ticket sales?   _____

38. Adam measures the length of his classroom with 30cm rulers. He lays
down 18 rulers. What is the length of his classroom in centimetres?   _____

39. A car travels 16 km per litre of petrol. It has 20 litres of petrol
in the tank. How far can it travel before it runs out of petrol?   _____   /4

> This graph shows the times of six riders in a cycle race.

40. Which cyclist finished first in the race? _____

41. Which cyclist finished 5 minutes behind Chris?

_____

42. Which cyclist finished 4 minutes behind Alan?

_____

43. How many cyclists finished between Fiona and Alan?

_____

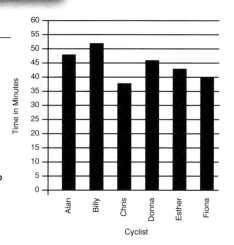

44. Write the cyclists in the order they finished.

/5

_____

What is the value of each letter?

45. $32 + c = 45$ $c =$ _____

46. $29 + g = 50$ $g =$ _____

47. $z - 15 = 9$ $z =$ _____

48. $27 - b = 19$ $b =$ _____   /4

49. Which line is perpendicular to AB? Tick the correct answer

   a) BG   **b)** CD   **c)** EF

50. Which line is parallel to AB? Tick the correct answer.

   a) BG   **b)** CD   **c)** EF   /2

/50

PAPER 12

1–6. Write these distances in centimetres.

$\frac{1}{2}$ metre   _____ $2\frac{1}{4}$ metres   _____ $\frac{3}{4}$ metre   _____

$1\frac{1}{2}$ metres   _____ $7\frac{3}{4}$ metres   _____ $4\frac{1}{2}$ metres   _____   /6

Answer these.

7.   19
    x 24

8.   53
    x 62

9.   38
    x 46

/3

10. A builder buys some floor tiles of two different weights. He buys five 3kg tiles and some $2\frac{1}{2}$kg tiles. He weighs the whole load and it totals 35kg. How many $2\frac{1}{2}$kg tiles does he buy?   _____   /1

11–19. Complete this chart showing the change for each item from £5, £10 and £20.

Change from:	£5	£10	£20
£1.30			
£4.25			
£2.77			

/9

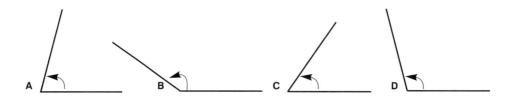

20–24. Estimate the size of each of these angles.

25–29. Measure each angle with a protractor.

Angle	A	B	C	D	E
Estimated size (°)					
Actual angle (°)					

/5

/5

Choose from these numbers to answer each question.

73   95   84   86   81

30. Which two numbers leave a remainder of 1 when divided by 5? _____

31. Which two numbers divide exactly by 3? _____

32. Which number leaves a remainder of 3 when divided by 4? _____

33. Which number can be divided exactly by both 6 and 7? _____

34. Which number leaves a remainder of 1 when divided by 3 or 6? _____

35. Which two numbers leave a remainder of 4 when divided by 7? _____   /6

Read these scales and write each weight in grams and kilograms.

36.

37.

38.

/3

_____ g = _____ kg   _____ g = _____ kg   _____ g = _____ kg

Maths 10–11 Answer booklet

PAPER 1

1. 3011
2–7. 82   93
    4.4   5.3
    14   7

8–10.
$$\begin{array}{r} 1\,7\,2 \\ +\,7\,5\,8 \\ \hline 9\,3\,0 \end{array}$$

11–18.

Shape	Name	Number of faces	Number of vertices	Number of edges
	Cuboid	6	8	12
	Cube	6	8	12
	Triangular prism	5	6	9

19. 920
20. 3050
21. 1680
22. 1050
23. 4.5kg
24. 1.7kg
25. $2\frac{4}{5}$ or $\frac{8}{10}$
26. $3\frac{2}{10}$
27. $15\frac{7}{10}$
28. $10\frac{3}{5}$ or $\frac{6}{10}$
29. $1\frac{9}{10}$
30.
31. 7.1   < $7\frac{7}{10}$
32. 14.5   > $14\frac{1}{5}$
33. $13\frac{3}{5}$ <   13.4
34. $9\frac{7}{10}$ > $7\frac{9}{10}$
35. 100
36. 600
37. 700
38. 2300
39. 200
40. 1500
41. 382
42. 413
43. 119

Bus Stop	time
44. 2	11.15
45. 3	11.30
46. 4	11.50
47. 5	11.55
48. 6	12.10

49. South
50. North

PAPER 2

1. 6451
2. 3729
3. 8504
4. 300g
5. 565
6. 807
7. 386
8. 332
9. 3.9
10. 5.6
11. 6.1
12. 27˚C   14˚C   –8˚C   –11˚C   –15˚C
13. 780, 425
14. 780
15. 425
16. 6 x 4   >   7 x 3
17. 8 x 6   >   5 x 9
18. 6 x 6   =   9 x 4
19. 7 x 5   >   4 x 8
20. $\frac{2}{3}$
21. $\frac{7}{10}$
22. 47
23–30.   7206   8206
      8705   8700
      34   14
      588   590
31. $\frac{3}{12}$
32. $\frac{2}{9}$ or $\frac{2}{12}$
33.

34.

35. 48cm
36. 19

37–39.

IN	37	53	79
OUT	74	106	158

40. 9+11+15 or 13+17+15 or 11+19+15
41. 266 + 84 or 265 + 85 or 264 + 86
42. 9100
43. 9910
44. 9010
45. 9991
46–47.
$$\begin{array}{r} 694 \\ -\,281 \\ \hline 413 \end{array} \qquad \begin{array}{r} 748 \\ -\,615 \\ \hline 133 \end{array}$$
48. Yes, 191 is in the counting pattern.
49. 8.20
50. 68p

PAPER 3

1. 385
2. 100
3. 345
4. £5008 and £6099
5. 28 jugs of water
6. Largest 0.9
7. Smallest 0.08
8. Largest $\frac{1}{3}$
9. Smallest $\frac{1}{12}$
10. Largest $\frac{7}{10}$
11. Smallest 0.25
12.

mirror line

13. 7˚C
14. –4˚C
15. c) 1 in 2
16. b) 1 in 3
17. d) 1 in 6
18. two thousand nine hundred
19. $\frac{2}{3} = \frac{8}{12}$
20. $\frac{4}{5} = \frac{8}{10}$
21. $\frac{3}{5} = \frac{9}{15}$
22. $\frac{3}{4} = \frac{9}{12}$
23.
$$\begin{array}{r} 4\,6\,3\,8 \\ +\,9\,1\,6\,3 \\ \hline 1\,3\,8\,0\,1 \end{array}$$
24. 19 – (12 – 5)
25. 22 – (5 + 5)
26. (6 + 13) – 7
27. (24 – 6) – 6
28. A: 165˚
29. B: 55˚
30. C: 70˚
31. D: 150˚
32. 1260g
33. 7.25
34. 4.3
35. 8.07
36. 9.19
37. 3774
38. 2778
39. 10415
40. 58.45m²
41. £194
42–45.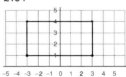
46. (–3, 4)
47. 2.92
48. 510g
49. 40%
50. 0.25

PAPER 4

1. 42
2. 54
3. $\frac{2}{3}$

4–9.

x	4	9	3
7	28	63	21
8	32	72	24
9	24	54	18

10. 777777
11. 333333
12. 888888
13. 555555
14. 3.9
15. 13.5
16–17.

$$\begin{array}{r} 3847 \\ -\,1762 \\ \hline 2085 \end{array} \qquad \begin{array}{r} 7943 \\ -\,2486 \\ \hline 5457 \end{array}$$

18. 27 ➔ (1,27) (3,9)
19. 50 ➔ (1,50) (2,25) (5,10)
20. 18 ➔ (1,18) (2,9) (3,6)
21. 54 ➔ (1,54) (2,27) (3,18) (6,9)
22–25.

IN	3	9	10	4
OUT	17	65	73	25

26–27. 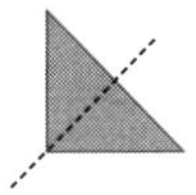 right-angled triangle

28–29. 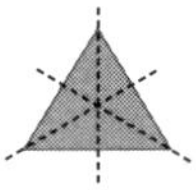 equilateral triangle

30. 350ml 0.5l 1.3l 1500ml 3300ml 3.5l
31–34.

	Multiple of 4	Not a multiple of 4
Factor of 60	12	30
Not a factor of 60	24	18

35. 4700
36. 12300
37. 416000
38. $5\frac{9}{100}$
39. 91.90
40. 40.68
41–48.

Angle	A	B	C	D
Acute	✓			✓
Obtuse		✓	✓	
Measured size (°)	45°	150°	110°	80°

49. area = 36 cm^2
50. area = 34 cm^2

PAPER 5

1. £8.91
2. £1.09
3. 8.6kg
4–5. Any 4 x 6 rectangle.
6. 46m
7. b) 6
8. 850g 8050g 8.2kg 8800g 85kg
9. $\frac{1}{2}$
10. $\frac{9}{10}$
11. $\frac{3}{5}$
12. $\frac{3}{4}$
13–18.

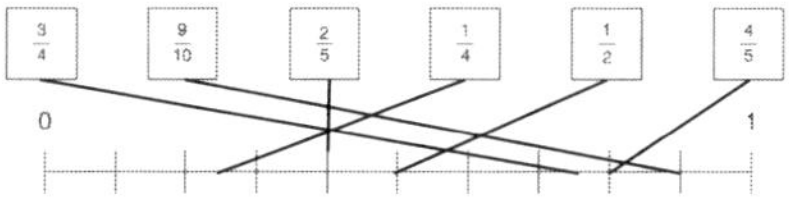

19. 50%
20. 25%
21. 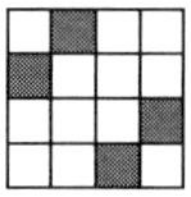

22. 234.5
23. 100
24. $\frac{1}{12}$ $\frac{1}{4}$ $\frac{1}{3}$ $\frac{2}{3}$ $\frac{3}{4}$
25. $\begin{array}{r} 29.53 \\ +\,15.14 \\ \hline 44.67 \end{array}$ **26.** $\begin{array}{r} 53.09 \\ -\,27.96 \\ \hline 25.13 \end{array}$
27. 237 ÷ 4
28. 60km
29. 1.30pm
30. 70km/h
31–33.

1	2	3	4	5
1	3	5	7	9

34. 900ml
35. £1.48
36. 7562 white shirts
37. 6065 cotton shirts
38. 7
39. 3
40–41. 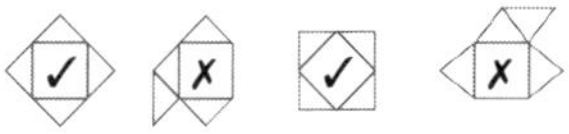

42. 12000g or 12kg
43. 3
44. 3
45. 12
46–49.

x	3	5
46	138	230
19	57	95

50. d) $\frac{3}{5}$

PAPER 6

1. b) £132
2–5. 9m 22cm 922cm
2m 80cm 280cm
3m 25cm 325cm
7m 5 cm 705cm
6m 9cm 609cm
6. 6cm (Accept 5.8cm to 6cm.)
7. 3m (Accept 2.9m to 3m.)
8. 1517
9. 263 r 1
10. $\frac{3}{4} > \frac{2}{3}$
11. $\frac{5}{6} < \frac{11}{12}$
12. $\frac{2}{6} = \frac{2}{3}$
13. $\frac{2}{3} > \frac{7}{12}$
14. c) 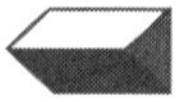

15. 5.30pm
16. 6.55am
17. a = 6
18. y = 32
19. c) 0.008
20. 7
21. 31
22. 6801
23. 29468
24–32.

	Round to the nearest 100	Round to the nearest 1000	Round to the nearest 10000
29832 ➔	29800	30000	30000
60157 ➔	60200	60000	60000
25129 ➔	25100	25000	30000

33.
480 478 **468** 474 472 470 **476**
3165 3150 3155 3160 **3145** 3170 3175

34. 2.30
35–38.

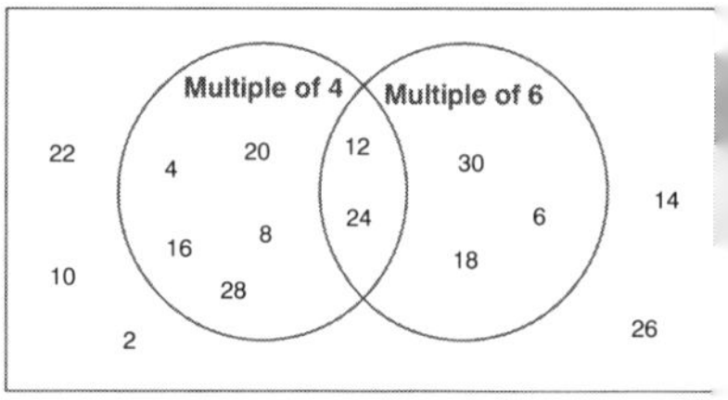

39. 8
40. 9
41. 9 and 12
42. 5 and 12
43. obtuse
44. right angle
45. obtuse
46. acute
47. right angle
48. acute
49. c) 72
50. 10122m

PAPER 7

1–6.
$3\,7 + 4\,8 = 8\,5$
$6\,2 + 2\,3 = 8\,5$
$2\,6 + 5\,9 = 8\,5$

7. 23 and 55
8. 74 and 82
9. 23 and 48
10. 9468
11. 7803
12. 4479
13. £20.24
14. £22.44
15. £16.23
16. AB is parallel to CD
17. HI is perpendicular to IJ
18. AB is perpendicular to BD
19. HL is parallel to JK
20. JK is perpendicular to KL
21. 16.18
22. 16.4
23. 16.53
24. 16.79
25. 16.85
26. 16.79
27. 35°
28. 80°
29. 150°
30. 130°
31.
32.
33.
34. 55mm = 5.5 cm
35. 10.64m = 1064 cm
36. 810cm = 0.81 m
37. 9.3km = 9300 m
38. 3200m = 3.2 km
39. 6.25m = 625 cm

40–43.

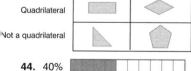

	Right angles	No right angles
Quadrilateral		
Not a quadrilateral		

44. 40%
45. 80%
46. 54 × 6 = 324
47. 21
48. Consecutive numbers are added: 3+**3** =6, 6+**4** = 10, 10+**5** = 15, so 15+ **6** is 21
49. 60 boys
50. 80 girls

PAPER 8

1. 7300
2. 7800
3. 19
4. 27
5. 20
6. 38
7. 12
8. 34kg
9. 45kg
10. 11:15
11. 21:55
12. 16:23
13. 08:57
14. 995m
15. 1381m
16. 37m
17. Atlantic Ocean and Pacific Ocean
18. $\frac{1}{3} = \frac{5}{15}$
19. $\frac{2}{5} = \frac{8}{20}$
20. $\frac{3}{10} = \frac{12}{40}$
21. $\frac{3}{8} = \frac{9}{24}$
22. 125°
23. 60°
24. 100°
25. 35°
26. 90°
27. 22, 24
28. 23, 25
29. 26
30. 700ml, 0.75 litres, 7 litres, 7.3 litres, 7500ml

31–40.

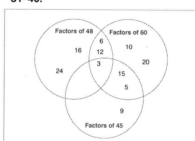

41. tetrahedron
42. cube
43. square based pyramid
44. triangular prism
45. square based pyramid
46. tetrahedron
47. triangular prism
48. cuboid
49. 31
50. 19

PAPER 9

1. 7595
2. 3287
3. 9105
4.
5. 1672
6. 9819
7. cuboid
8. triangular prism
9. cube
10. tetrahedron
11. square-based pyramid
12. 27.5
13. 28.1
14. 28.6
15. 29.7
16. $\frac{5}{15}$

17–25.

	Round to the nearest 10	Round to the nearest 100	Round to the nearest 1000
71653 →	71650	71700	72000
20983 →	20980	21000	21000
60057 →	60060	60100	60000

26. 9739
27. 8124
28. 5355
29. 400925
30. 118079
31. 400000
32. 290591
33. 330 golf balls
34. 5 times
35. 81962   81952   81942
36. 5011   5021   5031
37. 1972   2072   2172
38. 7254   7154   7054
39. 1, 2, 3, 6
40. 1, 3, 9, 27
41. 1, 5, 11, 55
42. 480 478 **476** 474 472 470 **468**
43. **3145** 3150 3155 3160 **3165** 3170 3175

44–47.

IN	23	37	51	80
OUT	920	1480	2040	3200

48. c) heptagon
49. 756 points
50. 453 points

PAPER 10

1. x10
2. x100
3. x10
4. x100
5. Area = 56cm²
Perimeter = 30cm
6. Area = 40cm²
Perimeter = 28cm
7. Area = 30cm²
Perimeter = 26cm

8–13.

Shape	A	B	C	D	E	F
Square			✓			
Rhombus						✓
Rectangle	✓					
Parallelogram				✓		
Trapezium					✓	
Kite		✓				

14. $\frac{1}{3} = \frac{2}{6} = \frac{3}{9} = \frac{4}{12} = \frac{5}{15}$
15. $\frac{3}{4} = \frac{6}{8} = \frac{9}{12} = \frac{12}{16} = \frac{15}{20}$
16. $\frac{4}{5} = \frac{8}{10} = \frac{12}{15} = \frac{16}{20} = \frac{20}{25}$
17. 45
18. 48
19. 90
20. 120
21.

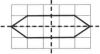

22. 18kg 705g
23. 7000
24. 94
25. 81
26. 110
27. 143
28. 9
29. 62
30. 18
31. $79 - 35 = 44$
32. 6.3
33. 23.9
34. 12.4
35. 18.5
36. $\frac{9}{4}$
37. $\frac{13}{3}$
38. $\frac{13}{8}$
39. 9523
40. 4055
41. 6078
42. 2587
43. $\frac{1}{3}$
44. $\frac{3}{4}$
45. $\frac{3}{4}$
46. $\frac{3}{5}$
47. $(12 \times 2) \div 3 = 8$
48. $42 - (2 \times 6) = 30$
49. $(8 \times 5) + (7 \times 3) = 61$
50. $(4 \times 4) - (54 \div 6) = 7$

PAPER 11
1. 0.3
2. 0.8
3. 0.05
4. 0.65
5. c) 5cm
6. 8653
7. 1364
8. 8612
9. 3246

10. 1.86m   >   1m 68cm
11. 1m 10cm   =   110cm
12. 472cm   >   2.74m
13. 3m 9cm   <   3.90m
14. 835cm   =   8m 35cm
15. 1.06m   <   160cm
16. 5.81m   >   1m 85cm
17. 46cm   >   0.42m
18. E square
19. D kite
20. A trapezium
21. B trapezium
22. C parallelogram
23. 965 copies
24. 70 copies
25. £16.16
26. £8.05
27. £3.95
28. £15.54
29. b)10
30. Goat A = 11kg   Goat B = 9kg

31.

32. 3.5cm   30cm   3.05m   350cm
33. 50g   250g $\frac{1}{2}$ kg   1.2kg
34. 600ml   6 litres   6600ml   60 litres
35. 400cm   40m   400m   4km
36. 600 minutes
37. £4850
38. 540cm
39. 320km
40. Chris
41. Esther
42. Billy
43. 2 cyclists
44. Chris, Fiona, Esther, Donna, Alan, Billy
45. c = 13
46. g = 21
47. z = 24
48. b = 8
49. Line EF
50. Line CD

PAPER 12
1. 50cm
2. 225cm
3. 75cm
4. 150cm
5. 775cm
6. 450cm
7. 456
8. 3286
9. 1748
10. 8 tiles

11–19.

Change from:	£5	£10	£20
£1.30	£3.70	£8.70	£18.70
£4.25	75p	£5.75	£15.75
£2.77	£2.33	£7.33	£17.33

20–24. Check estimates
25. 75°
26. 145°
27. 55°
28. 105°
29. 165°
30. 86 and 81
31. 84 and 81
32. 95
33. 84
34. 73
35. 95 and 81
36. 800g = 0.8kg
37. 1400g = 1.4kg
38. 1900g = 1.9kg
39. Check that a net of a cube has been drawn.
40–45.

+	62	35	49
34	96	69	83
38	100	73	87
61	123	96	110

46. 4cm
47. good chance
48. evens
49. impossible
50. certain

PAPER 13
1. 0.07   0.7   0.74   0.8
2. 0.09   0.11   0.25   0.8
3. 0.27   0.44   0.48   0.6
4. 0.03   0.2   0.23   0.32
5. £8.70
6. 1372m
7. 7050m
8. 5300m
9. 9000m
10–16.

You face	You turn	You now face
West	90° turn clockwise	North
East	180° turn anti-clockwise	West
South	90° turn anti-clockwise	East
North	270° turn clockwise	West
East	90° turn clockwise	South
South	180° turn anti-clockwise	North
West	270° turn anti-clockwise	North

17. $5\frac{9}{100}$
18. $\frac{1}{6}$
19. $\frac{1}{2}$
20. $\frac{1}{3}$
21. 0
22. 1
23. 52 weeks and 2 days left over

24. 41 tiles
25. 55 lengths and 5m left over
26. 42 egg boxes
27. 24cm
28. 1000
29. 1000
30. $\frac{2}{3}$
31. $\frac{3}{10}$
32. $\frac{5}{6}$
33. $\frac{4}{5}$
34. 720
35. 2394
36. 2340
37. $1\frac{1}{2}$
38. $1\frac{1}{4}$
39. $3\frac{1}{3}$
40. $7\frac{1}{2}$
41. $5\frac{1}{3}$
42. $2\frac{3}{4}$
43. equilateral triangle
44.
45. 1.5cm
46. 12cm
47–50. Answers may vary by 1mm.
A to C 2.7cm
A to D 3.5cm
A to E 3.9cm
A to F 3.6cm

PAPER 14
1. 27.93kg
2. 13.54kg
3. B and C
4. 7.81kg
5. b)
6. y = 38 z = 62
7. 1400ml = 1.4 litres
8. 600ml = 0.6 litres
9. 900ml = 0.9 litres
10. 1700ml = 1.7 litres
11. 36
12. 229g
13. 333ml
14. 269ml
15. $\frac{3}{4} > \frac{5}{8}$
16. $\frac{1}{12} < \frac{1}{2}$
17. $\frac{3}{4} > \frac{7}{12}$
18. $\frac{5}{6} > \frac{1}{6}$
19. $\frac{7}{8} > \frac{7}{12}$
20. $24\frac{4}{5}$
21. $7\frac{1}{5}$
22. $16\frac{7}{10}$
23. $20\frac{3}{5}$
24. $4\frac{9}{10}$
25. 13
26. 14
27. 29
28–33. $\frac{3}{6} = \frac{5}{10}$ or $\frac{3}{5} = \frac{6}{10}$ $\frac{1}{2} = \frac{4}{8}$ $\frac{2}{3} = \frac{8}{12}$
34. £63
35. £54
36. £36
37. £22.50

38. 2 lines
39. 1 line
40. 3 lines
41. 4 lines
42. 6 lines
43. 1 in 6 or $\frac{1}{6}$
44. 1 in 3 or $\frac{1}{3}$
45. 1 in 2 or $\frac{1}{2}$
46. 0 or impossible
47. Room A
48. 16:15
49. 55 minutes
50. 8.14pm

PAPER 15
1. a = 4
2. b = 8
3. c = 6
4. d = 5
5. c) remainder 3
6. True
7. True
8. True
9. True
10. 8.23
11. 21
12. 45
13. 8
14. 40
15. £63
16. 54kg
17. 12 red beads
18. 42 minutes
19. 15 oranges
20. 9 x (3 – 1) = 18
21. (4 x 5) + 9 = 29
22. 6 x (9 – 2) = 42
23. 30 ÷ (2 + 3) = 6
24. (60 ÷ 5) + 7 = 19
25. (48 ÷ 6) – 4 = 4
26. 2 bags of apples and 3 bags of grapes
27. b) 30
28. 1248
29. 3176
30. 12190
31. 30cm
32. $\frac{1}{10}$ $\frac{1}{5}$ $\frac{3}{5}$
33. $\frac{1}{4}$ $\frac{2}{5}$ $\frac{2}{3}$
34. $\frac{1}{6}$ $\frac{1}{4}$ $\frac{1}{2}$
35. $\frac{1}{5}$ $\frac{3}{4}$ $\frac{3}{4}$
36. 147 cars
37. a two → 1 in 6
38. an even number → 1 in 2

39. a multiple of 3 → 1 in 3
40. a number greater than 4 → 1 in 3
41. a number less than 4 → 1 in 2
42. under 2km
43. 9 children
44. 14 children
45. 15 children
46. 71 children
47. 176m²
48.
49. 90
50. 6

PAPER 16
1. 54
2. 20
3. 88
4. 63
5. 38
6. £224.35
7. 57 people
8. 932 stickers
9. £283
10. ÷ 100
11. ÷ 100
12. ÷ 10
13. ÷ 100
14. ÷ 10
15. ÷ 100
16. $\frac{28}{35}$ and $\frac{12}{15}$
17. $\frac{17}{20}$
18. $\frac{9}{21}$
19. $\frac{9}{36}$
20. 6100m
21. B and E
22. 11200m
23. From B to E then to D
24. D
25. B
26. White hat = £6
Red hat = £9
Green hat = £7
27–34. 89 85 81 77 73 69
265 240 215 190 165 140
381 370 359 348 337 326
130 138 146 154 162 170
35. £88
36. Andrew $\frac{18}{20}$ → 90%
37. Beth $\frac{7}{20}$ → 35%
38. Clare $\frac{38}{50}$ → 76%
39. David $\frac{21}{25}$ → 84%
40. Highest percentage → Andrew
41. 7.6 < 7.8 < 8.7 < 8.8
42. 23.4 > 19.3 > 19.2 > 13.9
43. (6,0)
44. (6,9)
45. 145 r 3
46. 66 r 1
47. 121 r 6

48. 180 r 1

49. 5, 7 and 9

50. 14 years old

PAPER 17

1. $\frac{1}{3}$

2. $\frac{3}{7}$

3. $\frac{1}{3}$

4. $\frac{7}{10}$

5. $\frac{1}{4}$

6. $\frac{3}{4}$

7. 54cm

8. 16:15

9. 14:20

10. 10:45

11. 19:25

12. 06:45

13. 1 in 2 or $\frac{1}{2}$

14. 2 litres

15. 6 glasses

16–20.

IN	23	51	62	39	80
OUT	1150	2550	3100	1950	4000

21–26.

+	3.4	6.2	5.8
3.6	7	9.8	9.4
5.6	9	11.8	11.4
3.3	6.7	9.5	9.1

27. 99

28. 118 r 3

29. remainder 2

30. 79 r 2

31. 600m

32. 7300m

33. 3900m

34. 3500m

35. 100m

36. 2300m

37. 16

38. 5 x 5p coins and 8x10p coins

39. 72   144

40. 208   416

41. 256   512

42.

43. 1.6kg

44.

45–47. prime numbers: 5, 17, 19, 23

48–50.

acute   obtuse   reflex

PAPER 18

1. 4.1 and 1.6

2. 7.3

3. 2.7 and 1.6

4. 7.9

5. £24

6. 23   17   11   5   −1   −7

7. −15   −11   −7   −3   1   5

8. 26   15   4   −7   −18   −29

9. −21   −16   −11   −6   −1   4

10. y = 9

11. b = 12

12. n = 8

13. t = 9

14. $\frac{9}{10}$

15. $\frac{7}{1000}$

16. $\frac{3}{100}$

17. $\frac{68}{100}$

18. 36 and 64

19. A = 33

20. B = 27

21. £8.10

22. 8.4 litres

23. 19.5m

24. 6.8kg

25. 42.1km

26. 38m

27. 114m

28. 140˚

29. 50˚

30. 70˚

31. Jug A

32. b) 6

33. 11 children

34. 24 children

35. 14 children

36. 8

37. 20

38. 24

39. 90

40. 35

41. 64

42. 1260

43. 2006

44. 2294

45. 109 r 4

46. 49 r 5

47. 84

48–50.

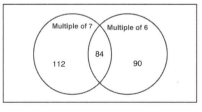

PAPER 19

1. 15˚

2. 22˚

3. 5˚

4. $\frac{8}{9}, \frac{2}{3}, \frac{6}{9}, \frac{3}{8}$ or $\frac{3}{8}$

5. $\frac{2}{9}$

6. $\frac{2}{3}$ or $\frac{6}{9}$

7. $\frac{4}{5} = 0.8 = 80\%$

8. $\frac{1}{4} = 0.25 = 25\%$

9. $\frac{1}{20} = 0.05 = 5\%$

10. $\frac{7}{10} = 0.7 = 70\%$

11. $\frac{1}{50} = 0.02 = 2\%$

12–14. 3   7   11   15   19

15. 1, 2, 4

16. 1, 3, 5, 15

17. 1, 2, 3, 6, 9, 18

18. 4

19. 15

20. 18

21. 15 litres

22. 0.18

23. £8

24. 3 x 5 x 11 = 165

25. 10.3 and 6.5

26. 516, 380

27. 516

28. 562, 547

29. 380, 485

30–33. square based pyramid, triangular prism, cuboid, tetrahedron

34–36. (−3,0), (1,2) and −1,−4)

37.

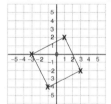

38. 122˚

39. 88˚

40. 75˚

41. 127˚

42. 0.18 and 0.82

43.

44. (9,3)

45. (18,6)

46. 1.3m

47. 18 pints

48. 67.5cm

49. 1 in 3 or $\frac{1}{3}$

50. 1 in 5 or $\frac{1}{5}$

PAPER 20

1. £1.30

2.

3–5. 7   16   25   34   43   52

6. 33 children

7. 40km

8. 11.00

9. 10km

10. 44km/h

11. B = 21

12. Box of 12 pens: £16.80. Buy 1 box, get 1 box half price (£1.05 each compared to £1.10 each for the other offer.)

13. 3.74 < 4.47 < 4.73 < 7.43

14. 29.7 > 29.11 > 22.52 > 22.3

15. 30cm

16. 9ml

17. £43

18. 28g

19. 15km

20. $\frac{14}{35}$

21. $\frac{5}{7}$

22. $\frac{3}{7}$

23. $\frac{77}{110}$

24–27.

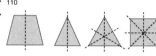

28. 7

29. 5

30. 8

31. 10

32–35.

$$5619 + 3658 = 9277$$

$$5848 + 3564 = 9412$$

$$2916 + 4616 = 6732$$

$$5293 + 3796 = 9089$$

36. 171m²

37. (19 − 8) - 4 = 7

38. 31 − (9 + 3) = 19

39. (19 − 4) + 8 = 23

40. 18 − (4 + 9) = 5

41. (15 − 9) x 4 = 24

42. 6 + (3 x 8) = 30

43. 8 and -11

44. 9.6m

45–47. p = 53°   r = 37°   q = 53°

48. 37

49. 140

50. 374

PAPER 21

1. $\frac{1}{5}$

2. $\frac{1}{4}$

3. $\frac{3}{4}$

4. $\frac{1}{20}$

5. $\frac{1}{10}$

6. $\frac{5}{6}$ of 30 > $\frac{4}{5}$ of 30

7. $\frac{5}{8}$ of 32 < $\frac{3}{4}$ of 32

8. $\frac{2}{3}$ of 60 > $\frac{3}{5}$ of 60

9. $\frac{3}{4}$ of 48 < $\frac{5}{6}$ of 48

10. $\frac{6}{7}$ of 28 > $\frac{3}{4}$ of 28

11. 36°

12. 156.25cm

13. 19cm

14. 3:2

15. 72g

16. 9

17. £112.50

18. 224 112 56 28 14 7 3.5

19. 352 176 88 44 22 11 5.5

20. 608 304 152 76 38 19 9.5

21. 8.5 litres

22. 15.9m

23. 9.3kg

24. 52.9km

25. £1.05

26. 5, 7, 8

27. 17050

28. 11878

29. 2353

30. 739

31. 56cm²

32. 51cm²

33. y = 6

34. h = 7

35. v = 9

36. g = 8

37–41. a multiple of 2 → Evens
a diamond → certain
a multiple of 5 → poor chance
a number greater than 3 → good chance
the queen of diamonds → impossible

42. $\frac{6}{9}$ or $\frac{2}{3}$

43. $\frac{9}{12}$ or $\frac{3}{4}$

44. $\frac{6}{12}$ or $\frac{1}{2}$

45. $\frac{3}{15}$ or $\frac{1}{3}$

46. 1:2

47. 1:3

48. 1:1

49. 2:1

50. 466g

PAPER 22

1. 2.31 2.32 2.33 2.34 2.35 2.36

2. 9.059 9.06 9.061 9.062 9.063 9.064

3. 14.75 14.76 14.77 14.78 14.79 14.8

4. 4.9 x 10 = 49

5. 6.13 x 100 = 613

6. 93.77 x 100 = 9377

7. 194.5 ÷ 100 = 1.945

8. 9061 ÷ 100 = 90.61

9. 373 ÷ 10 = 37.3

10. 40 minutes

11. 1 hour 22 minutes

12. 3 hours 36 minutes

13. 1 hour 12 minutes

14. 2, 4, 5

15. 2, 3, 4, 6

16. 2, 3, 4, 6, 9

17. 3, 5, 9

18. 2, 3, 5, 6, 9

19. 94°

20. 18°

21. 23°

22. rotated

23. reflected

24. translated

25. 3cm²

26. 8cm²

27. 22.5cm²

28. 20 boys

29. 35 balloons

30. 88cm

31. Bilston FC

32. 9 matches drawn

33. $\frac{1}{3}$

34. 42cm²

35. 39cm²

36. £219.60

37. 5 x 7 x 13 = 455

38. 13

39. (1, 54) (2, 27) (3, 18) (6, 9)

40. 7254

41. 4828

42. 18980

43–45. 1 cake = 75p
1 sandwich = £1.45
1 sausage roll = £1.10

46. True

47. False

48. False

49. True

50. 81cm²

PAPER 23

1. 16cm

2. 12km

3. 15kg

4. 9ml

5. 45mm

6. 21m

7–14.

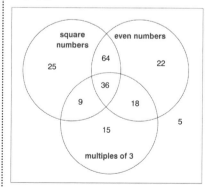

15–17. £151.37 + £48.63
£115.47 + £84.53
£155.43 + £44.57

18. 63km

19. 6.3g

20. 630 litres

21. 63m

22. 6.3kg

23. 6.3cm
24. 144
25. 49
26. 4
27. 8
28. 1
29. 88cm²
30. 93cm²
31. 75% = $\frac{3}{4}$
32. 20% < 1/2
33. $\frac{3}{5}$ > 30%
34. 6% < 1/6
35. $\frac{9}{100}$ < 0.9
36. (0,5), (4,5) and (4,8)
37.

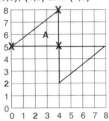

38. rotation
39–41. triangular prism, hexagonal prism, squared based pyramid
42. 102°
43. 72°
44. 54°
45. 42°
46. 1, 2, 3, 6
47. 1, 3, 9
48. 1, 2, 3, 5, 6, 10, 15, 30
49. 20:18
50. 6 ice-creams and 4 lollies

PAPER 24
1. 3.7 x 10 = 37
2. 9.23 x 10 = 923
3. 86.07 x 100 = 8607
4. 158.1 ÷ 10 = 15.81
5. 397.6 ÷ 100 = 3.976
6. 9864 ÷ 100 = 98.64
7. 44   29   14   −1   −16
8. −17   −11   −5   1   7
9. −14   −5   4   13   22
10. 31   18   5   −8   −21
11. 22:13
12.

13. 1.039
14. 1.028
15. 0.932
16. 32
17. 110°
18. 30°
19. 230°
20. −20 and −110

21. 24
22. 36
23. 15
24. 21°
25. $\frac{1}{4}$ $\frac{3}{5}$ $\frac{13}{20}$ $\frac{7}{10}$ $\frac{3}{4}$
26. 80cm
27. 3 and 18 or 9 and 12
28–31. 415 x 16 = 6640
        74 x 39 = 2886
32. 20% of 80 is 16
33. 20% of 400 is 80
34. (38, 21)
35. (28, 25)
36. 6cm
37. 30 days
38. 10 ounces
39. 475g
40. 12cm
41–46.

	Packed lunch	School dinner	Total
Boys	42	30	72
Girls	29	57	86
Total	71	87	158

47. A carton holds more: 345ml
48. 49
49. 43
50. 44

39. These three nets fold up to make a cube. Draw a new net of a cube that is different to these.

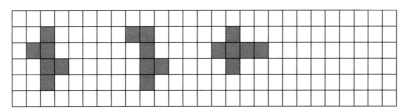

/1

40–45. Write the missing numbers on this addition grid.

+	62	35	49
34		69	
38	100		
61			110

/6

46. The area of a square is 16cm². What is the length of each side? _____

/1

47–50. What is the chance of picking out the number **3** in each set?
Join each set to the correct statement.

> impossible   poor chance   evens   good chance   certain

3 3 3
3 3 1
1 2 2

3 3 3 3 3
1 1 1 2 2

1 1 1
1 2 2
2 4 4

3 3 3
3 3 3

/4

/50

PAPER 13

> Write each set in order, starting with the smallest.

1.   0.07   0.74   0.7   0.8   _____

2.   0.25   0.09   0.8   0.11   _____

/4

3.   0.44   0.6   0.27   0.48   _____

4.   0.32   0.23   0.03   0.2   _____

5. Two items cost a total of £28.50. If one of the items costs £19.80, what is the cost of the other item? Tick the correct answer.

    a) £9.70   **b)** £9.30   **c)** £8.70   **d)** £8.30

 /1

> Write these in metres.

6. 1km 372m = _____m   **7.** 7km 50m = _____m

8. 5km 300m = _____m   **9.** 9km = _____m

/4

10–16. Complete this chart.

You face	You turn	You now face
West	90° turn clockwise	
East	180° turn anti-clockwise	
South	90° turn anti-clockwise	
North	270° turn clockwise	
East	90° turn clockwise	
South	180° turn anti-clockwise	
West	270° turn anti-clockwise	

/7

17. What is 5.09 as a fraction? Tick the correct answer.

    a) $5\frac{9}{10}$ **b)** $5\frac{9}{100}$ **c)** $5\frac{90}{100}$ **d)** $5\frac{90}{1000}$

/1

> On a 1–6 dice, what is the probability of throwing the following numbers? Choose your answers from these possibilities.

$$1 \quad \frac{1}{3} \quad \frac{1}{2} \quad \frac{1}{6} \quad 0$$

18. a four   _____   **19.** an odd number   _____

20. a number smaller than 3   _____   **21.** a number greater than 7   _____

22. a number between 0 and 7   _____

 /5

Answer these.

23. There are 366 days in a leap year. How many full weeks
are in a leap year and how many days are left over? _____

24. A floor is 324cm long and floor tiles are 8cm in length. How many
tiles will be needed to cover one whole length of the floor? _____

25. A reel of electric cable is 500m in length. It is cut into 9m lengths.
How many 9m lengths will there be and how much is left over? _____

26. A farmer collects 249 eggs and puts them into egg boxes
that hold 6 eggs. All the eggs must be in an egg box.
How many egg boxes will he need? _____ /4

27. The perimeter of a square is 96cm. What is the length of each side? _____ /1

28–29. What are the missing numbers? $780 \div \boxed{} = 0.78$ $0.06 \times \boxed{} = 60$ /2

30–33. Reduce each of these fractions to their simplest form.

$$\frac{20}{30} \rightarrow \frac{\boxed{}}{\boxed{}} \qquad \frac{9}{30} \rightarrow \frac{\boxed{}}{\boxed{}} \qquad \frac{10}{12} \rightarrow \frac{\boxed{}}{\boxed{}} \qquad \frac{16}{20} \rightarrow \frac{\boxed{}}{\boxed{}}$$ /4

Answer these.

34. What is 45 multiplied by 16? _____

35. What is the product of 42 and 57? _____

36. What is 90 multiplied by 26? _____ /3

37–42. Change these improper fractions to mixed numbers.

$$\frac{3}{2} = \text{_____} \qquad \frac{5}{4} = \text{_____} \qquad \frac{10}{3} = \text{_____}$$

$$\frac{15}{2} = \text{_____} \qquad \frac{16}{3} = \text{_____} \qquad \frac{11}{4} = \text{_____}$$ /6

43. What is the name of this shape? Tick the correct answer.

a) isosceles triangle ☐   **b)** scalene triangle ☐

c) equilateral triangle ☐   **d)** right-angled triangle ☐

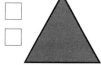

/1

44. Tick the shape that has 6 vertices.

a)   b)   c)   d)

/1

This is a regular octagon.

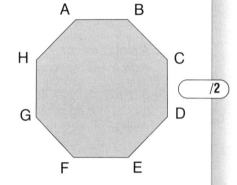

45. What is the length of each side? _____

46. What is the perimeter of the octagon? _____

/2

47–50. Measure these distances on the octagon to the nearest millimetre:

A to C _____   A to D _____

A to E _____   A to F _____

/4

/50

PAPER 14

Look at these boxes and answer the questions.

         11.64kg

A   B   C   D

1. What is the total weight of the two heaviest boxes? _____

2. What is the difference in weight between the heaviest and lightest boxes? _____

3. Which two boxes total 11.23kg? _____

4. What is the difference in weight between boxes A and B? _____

/4

5. Which of these is an isosceles triangle? Tick the correct answer.

a)   b)  c)

/1

6. y and z each stand for whole numbers.

y + z = 100. z is 24 more than y. What is the value of y and z?

y = _____   z = _____

/1

> Write the amount of water in each jug as millilitres and litres.

7.    **8.**   **9.**   **10.**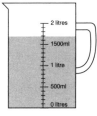

_____ ml = _____ l   _____ ml = _____ l   _____ ml = _____ l   _____ ml = _____ l

/4

11. I'm thinking of a number. If I halve the number and then add 12, the answer is 30. What number am I thinking of?   _____

12. 687g of sugar is divided into 3 bags. How much will one bag of sugar weigh?   _____

13. 1332ml of soup is shared equally between 4 bowls. How much soup will there be in each bowl?   _____

14. A jug holding 1345ml of water is poured equally into 5 glasses. How much water will there be in each glass?   _____

/4

15–19. Write the missing < or > to make each sentence true.

$\frac{3}{4} \square \frac{5}{8}$ $\frac{1}{12} \square \frac{1}{2}$ $\frac{3}{4} \square \frac{7}{12}$ $\frac{5}{6} \square \frac{1}{6}$ $\frac{7}{8} \square \frac{7}{12}$

/5

20–24. Write these decimals as mixed numbers.

24.8 = _____   7.2 = _____   16.7 = _____   20.6 = _____   4.9 = _____

/5

Answer these.

25. 70 ⟌ 910   **26.** 60 ⟌ 840   **27.** 30 ⟌ 870   /3

28–33. The digits **2, 3, 4, 5, 6** and **8** are missing from these equivalent fractions.

Write them with the digits in the correct place.

$$\frac{3}{\Box} = \frac{\Box}{10} \qquad \frac{1}{\Box} = \frac{\Box}{8} \qquad \frac{2}{\Box} = \frac{\Box}{12}$$

/6

In a sale, everything is reduced by 10%. Write the cost of each item.

34.

WAS
£70
Now
10% off

Sale Price:

_____

35.

£60
Less
10%

Sale Price:

_____

36.

WAS
£40
10%
discount
today

Sale Price:

_____

37.

£25
Special
offer 10%
off

Sale Price:

_____

/4

38–42. Draw all of the lines of symmetry on these shapes and write the number of lines of symmetry.

_____ lines of symmetry

 _____ lines of symmetry

 _____ lines of symmetry

 _____ lines of symmetry

 _____ lines of symmetry

/5

On this spinner, what is the chance of spinning:

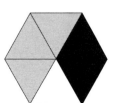

43. white?   _____

44. black?   _____

45. grey?   _____

46. blue?   _____

/4

47. Which has the largest area, Room A or Room B? _____

Room A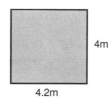

3.5m

5m

Room B

4m

4.2m

/1

48. A football match starts at 14:45 and lasts
an hour and a half. What time will the match end? _____

49. A school lunchtime is from twenty-five past twelve until
twenty past one. How many minutes is this school lunchtime? _____

50. A train should arrive at 7.50pm but it is 24 minutes late.
What time does the train arrive? _____ /3

/50

PAPER 15

1–4. Complete these.

$$4a + 2 = 18 \qquad 3b + 7 = 31 \qquad 4c - 5 = 19 \qquad 5d - 8 = 17$$

$$a = \text{\_\_\_\_\_} \qquad b = \text{\_\_\_\_\_} \qquad c = \text{\_\_\_\_\_} \qquad d = \text{\_\_\_\_\_}$$

/4

5. What is the remainder when 345 is divided by 6? Circle the correct answer.

a) 1 **b)** 2 **c)** 3 **d)** 4

/1

For each statement tick (✓) True or False.

6. A trapezium always has a pair of parallel lines. True ☐ False ☐

7. A kite sometimes has a right angle. True ☐ False ☐

8. A parallelogram always has opposite sides of equal length. True ☐ False ☐

9. A rhombus always has pairs of opposite angles the same size. True ☐ False ☐

/4

10. My watch shows 8.03 and is ten minutes slow. My alarm clock is ten minutes fast. What time will be shown on my alarm clock? _____ /1

Work out the mystery number for each of these.

11. When I double my number, and then add 3, the answer is 45. _____

12. When I divide my number by 5, and then add 6, the answer is 15. _____

13. When I multiply my number by 3, and then subtract 20, the answer is 4. _____

14. When I divide my number by 4, and then subtract 5, the answer is 5. _____ /4

Read and answer these.

15. Jack has £84. He spends $\frac{3}{4}$ of his money on a new CD player. How much does the CD player cost? _____

16. What is $\frac{9}{10}$ of 60kg? _____

17. A bag has 32 beads in it. $\frac{3}{8}$ of the beads are red. How many beads are red? _____

18. How many minutes are there in $\frac{7}{10}$ of one hour? _____

19. There are 25 oranges on a market stall. Mrs Andrews buys $\frac{3}{5}$ of the oranges. How many does she buy? _____ /5

20–25. Draw brackets to make each number sentence true.

$9 \times 3 - 1 = 18$ $4 \times 5 + 9 = 29$ $6 \times 9 - 2 = 42$

$30 \div 2 + 3 = 6$ $60 \div 5 + 7 = 19$ $48 \div 6 - 4 = 4$ /6

26. A bag of apples costs 75p. A bag of grapes costs 90p.

Anil bought some bags of apples and grapes. He spent £4.20.

How many bags of each type of fruit did he buy? _____ /1

27. What is the missing number? Circle the correct answer. $70 \times \boxed{} = 2100$ /1

a) 3 b) 30 c) 300 d) 3000

Answer these.

28. 78
    x 16
    _____

    _____

29. 397
    x 8
    _____

    _____

30. 530
    x 23
    _____

    _____

/3

31. The area of a rectangle is 56cm². One of the sides is 8cm. What is the perimeter of the rectangle? _____ /1

> Write each set of fractions in order, starting with the smallest.

32. $\frac{3}{5}$ $\frac{1}{2}$ $\frac{1}{10}$ _____

33. $\frac{1}{4}$ $\frac{5}{8}$ $\frac{2}{3}$ _____

34. $\frac{1}{2}$ $\frac{1}{6}$ $\frac{1}{4}$ _____

35. $\frac{3}{8}$ $\frac{3}{4}$ $\frac{1}{5}$ _____ /4

36. Robert has a collection of toy cars that he wants to count. He knows that he has between 120 and 150 cars, but not the exact number. He decides to count them in fives, and he has 2 left over. He then counts them in sixes and he has 3 left over.

Can you work out exactly how many cars Robert has? _____ /1

> Write down the chance of throwing each of the numbers below on a dice. Choose from → **1 in 2** **1 in 3** **1 in 6**.

37. a two _____

38. an even number _____

39. a multiple of 3 _____

40. a number greater than 4 _____ /5

41. a number less than 4 _____

> Look at the graph and answer these.

42. Which distance did the largest number of children travel to school? _____

43. How many children travelled between 6–8km to school? _____

44. Half of the children travelling under 2km walk to school. How many children walk to school? _____

45. How many children in total travel over 6km to school? _____

46. How many students in total took part in this survey? _____ /5

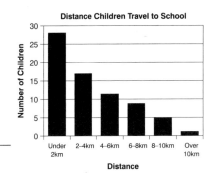

Distance Children Travel to School

47. What is the area of the garden that is grass? _____ /1

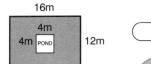

48. Shade some squares to make a reflection on the mirror line.

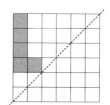

/1

Write the next numbers in these sequences.

49.   58   66   74   82 _____   **50.**   66   51   36   21 _____   /2

/50

PAPER 16

1–5. Write the answer for each of these.

(64 – 19) + 9 = _____   83 – (34 + 29) = _____   (57 – 13) x 2 = _____

92 – (47 – 18) = _____   (7 x 9) – (53 – 28) = _____   /5

Answer these problems.

6. A greenhouse costs £189.95. It costs an extra
£34.40 to have it delivered. What will the total cost be?   _____

7. Becky makes 171 sandwiches for a party. She has
made 3 sandwiches per person.
How many people are expected at the party?   _____

8. Sam needs another 68 stickers to have 1000
in his collection. How many stickers does he have?   _____

9. The cost of a holiday is £759 in April and £1042 in July.
What is the difference in cost between the two months?   _____   /4

10–15. Write the missing ÷10 or ÷100 in each of these.

790 → ☐ → 7.9   40 → ☐ → 0.4   86 → ☐ → 8.6

29 → ☐ → 0.29   145 → ☐ → 14.5   7 → ☐ → 0.07   /6

Look at these fractions and answer the questions.

16. Which two fractions are equivalent? _____

17. Which fraction is in its simplest form? _____

18. Which fraction simplifies to $\frac{3}{7}$? _____

19. Which fraction is equivalent to $\frac{1}{4}$? _____

$\frac{28}{35}$	$\frac{16}{30}$	$\frac{17}{20}$
$\frac{9}{21}$	$\frac{12}{15}$	$\frac{9}{36}$

/4

Look at the map and answer these.

20. How many metres is it from B to C? _____

21. Which two places are 6500m from each other?

_____

22. How many metres is it in total for the shortest
route from D to A? _____

23. What is the shortest route from B to D? _____

24–25. In which places on the map would you see these road-signs?

C 4700m | E 3800m

A 5600m   C 6100m   E 6500m

_____   _____

/4

/2

26. Rosie bought three different hats. The red hat and the green
hat cost a total of £16. The white hat and the green hat cost
a total of £13. The white hat and the red hat cost a total of £15.
What is the cost of each hat? red = _____ green = _____ white = _____

/1

Write the missing numbers in these sequences.

27–28. 89 ☐ 81 ☐ 73 69   **29–30.** 265 ☐ ☐ 190 165 140

31–32. 381 370 ☐ 348 ☐ 326   **33–34.** ☐ 138 146 154 162 ☐

/8

35. A jacket costs £68 and a pair of shoes costs £42.
There is a 20% sale on these items. What will the total cost be in the sale? _____

/1

Change these maths test scores to percentages.

36. Andrew $\dfrac{18}{20}$ → _____%

37. Beth $\dfrac{7}{20}$ → _____%

38. Clare $\dfrac{38}{50}$ → _____%

39. David $\dfrac{21}{25}$ → _____%

40. Which child has the highest percentage score? _____

/5

Write each set of decimals in order in the boxes to make these correct.

41. 8.7   7.8   7.6   8.8   ☐ < ☐ < ☐ < ☐

42. 23.4   13.9   19.3   19.2   ☐ > ☐ > ☐ > ☐

/2

43. X, Y and Z are corners of a rectangle.
What are the coordinates of the fourth corner?

_____

44. A, B and C are corners of a parallelogram.
What are the coordinates of the fourth corner?

_____

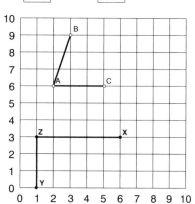

/2

Calculate the answer for each of these. Show your method.

45. 5 | 7 2 8   **46.** 6 | 3 9 7   **47.** 7 | 8 5 3   **48.** 4 | 7 2 1   /4

49. Circle the numbers that are **not** factors of 48.   1   2   3   4   5   6   7   8   9   /1

50. Alice's father was 33 when she was born. Three years ago he was four times as old as Alice. How old is Alice now?   /1

_____

/50

PAPER 17

1–6. Write these fractions in their simplest form.

$$\frac{30}{90} \quad \square\!\!\!\square \qquad \frac{12}{28} \quad \square\!\!\!\square \qquad \frac{15}{45} \quad \square\!\!\!\square \qquad \frac{21}{30} \quad \square\!\!\!\square \qquad \frac{8}{32} \quad \square\!\!\!\square \qquad \frac{12}{16} \quad \square\!\!\!\square$$

/6

7. Two poles are 1.35m and 1.89m in length. What is the difference in their length?

_____ cm

/1

8–12. Write these times using the 24–hour clock.

quarter past 4 in the afternoon _____

20 minutes past 2 in the afternoon _____

quarter to 11 in the morning _____

25 minutes past 7 in the evening _____

quarter to 7 in the morning _____

/5

13. A coin is tossed 20 times and lands heads up for the last 5 throws.
What probability is there that it will land heads up on the 21st throw? _____

/1

14. How much fruit drink is made in total? _____ litres

15. How many 300ml glasses can be filled? _____

Fruit Drink
1.2 litres orange juice
300ml lemonade
250ml apple juice
250ml pineapple juice

/2

16–20. This function machine multiplies by 50. Complete the table
of results for the numbers coming out of the function machine.

IN) **x 50** (OUT

IN	23	51	62	39	80
OUT					

/5

21–26. Write the missing numbers on this addition grid.

Read and answer these.

+	3.4	6.2	5.8
3.6		9.8	
5.6			
3.3	6.7		9.1

27. Divide 297 by 3. _____

/6

28. What is 475 divided by 4? _____

29. What is the remainder when 395 is shared between 3? _____

/4

30. What is 397 divided by 5? _____

31–36. Write these in metres.

0.6km _____ metres   7.3km _____ metres   3.9km _____ metres

$3\frac{1}{2}$ km _____ metres $\frac{1}{10}$ km _____ metres $2\frac{3}{10}$ km _____ metres   /6

37. I'm thinking of a number. If I halve the number and then add 9, the answer is 17. What number am I thinking of? _____   /1

38. Joseph has some 5p and 10p coins. He has three more 10p coins than 5p coins and altogether he has £1.05. How many of each coin does he have? _____   /1

39–41. In these sequences each number is double the previous number. Write the missing numbers.

9   18   36   ☐ ☐   26   52   104   ☐ ☐

32   64   128   ☐ ☐   /3

42. Put a tick (✓) in the right-angled triangle.   /1

43. What is the weight of the flour on Scale A?

_____   /1

44. Scale B has the exact amount of flour as Scale A. Draw an arrow on Scale B to the same weight as Scale A.   /1

A   B

45–47. Draw a circle around the prime numbers.

5   16   17   18   19   20   21   22   23   /3

48–50. Label these angles as **acute, obtuse** or **reflex.**

_____   _____   _____   /3

/50

PAPER 18

Use these numbers to answer the following: 9.5   2.7   4.1   7.3   1.6

1. Which two numbers have a difference of 2.5? _____

2. Which number is 2.2 less than the greatest number? _____

3. Which two numbers have a difference of 1.1? _____

4. What is the answer if you subtract the smallest
number from the greatest number? _____   /4

5. Kate went shopping with £60 to spend on some clothes. She spent $\frac{3}{5}$ of
her money in one shop. How much money did she have left? _____   /1

Write the missing numbers in these sequences.

6. ☐   17   11   5   –1   ☐   7.   –15   ☐   ☐   –3   1   5

8.   26   15   ☐   –7   ☐   –29   9.   –21   ☐   –11   ☐   –1   4   /4

Write the value of each letter.

10. $y + 29 = 38$ y = _____   11. $30 - b = 18$ b = _____

12. $7n = 56$ n = _____   13. $36 \div t = 4$ t = _____   /4

Circle the fraction that is the same as each decimal number.

14.   0.9 $\frac{9}{10}$ $\frac{9}{100}$ $\frac{9}{1000}$ 15.   0.007 $\frac{7}{10}$ $\frac{7}{100}$ $\frac{7}{1000}$

16.   0.03 $\frac{3}{10}$ $\frac{3}{100}$ $\frac{3}{1000}$ 17.   0.68 $\frac{68}{10}$ $\frac{68}{100}$ $\frac{68}{1000}$ /4

18. Which two square numbers total 100?   _____   _____   /1

19–20. A and B are two different whole numbers. A + B = 60. A is 6 greater than B.

What are the numbers A and B?   A = _____   B = _____   /2

21–25. Round each amount to the nearest tenth.

£8.07 → _____   8.369 litres → _____   19.51m → _____

6.847 kg → _____   42.09km → _____

/5

> The area of a rectangle garden is 722m². The shorter side is 19m in length.

26. What is the length of the longer side? _____

27. What is the perimeter of the garden? _____

/2

> What is the angle marked x in each shape?

28.
angle x =

_____

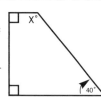

29.
angle x =

_____

30.
angle x =

_____

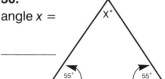

/3

31. Which jug contains more water, Jug A or Jug B? _____

/1

32. What is the missing number? Circle the correct answer.

($\square$ + 9) x 6 = 90

a) 8   **b)** 6   **c)** 7   **d)** 3

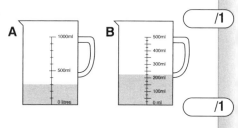

/1

/1

> A computer game has 30 levels of difficulty until it is completed. This graph shows the number of levels reached on the game by a group of children

33. How many children reached between 21 and 25 levels? _____

34. How many children completed up to 15 levels?

_____

35. How many children reached level 21 or higher?

_____

/3

52

Complete these.

36. $\frac{1}{10}$ of 40 = $\frac{1}{2}$ of _____   **37.** $\frac{1}{4}$ of 16 = $\frac{1}{5}$ of _____   **38.** $\frac{1}{2}$ of 12 = $\frac{1}{4}$ of _____

39. $\frac{1}{3}$ of 27 = $\frac{1}{10}$ of _____   **40.** $\frac{1}{6}$ of 42 = $\frac{1}{5}$ of _____   **41.** $\frac{1}{5}$ of 40 = $\frac{1}{8}$ of _____   /6

Answer these.

42.   28
        x 45
        _____

        _____

43.   34
        x 59
        _____

        _____

44.   62
        x 37
        _____

        _____   /3

Answer these.

45.   6 ⟌ 6 5 8   **46.**   8 ⟌ 3 9 7   **47.**   9 ⟌ 7 5 6   /3

48–50. Write each of these three numbers in the correct place on this Venn diagram.

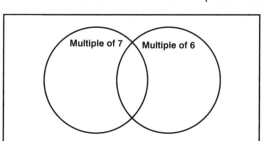

112
90
84

Multiple of 7   Multiple of 6

/3

/50

PAPER 19

What is the difference in temperature between these pairs of thermometers?

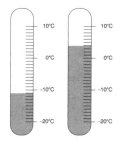   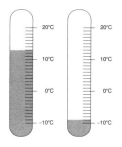   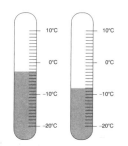

/3

1. _____   **2.** _____   **3.** _____

Look at these number cards.

| 8 | 2 | 9 | 3 | 6 |

4–6. Use any two number cards to complete each of these:

$$\frac{\square}{\square} > \frac{1}{3} \qquad \frac{\square}{\square} < \frac{1}{4} \qquad \frac{\square}{\square} = \frac{2}{3}$$

/3

7–11. Write the missing numbers to complete these.

$$\frac{4}{\square} = 0.\square = 80\% \qquad \frac{\square}{4} = 0.25 = \square\% \qquad \frac{1}{20} = 0.05 = \square\%$$

$$\frac{7}{\square} = 0.7 = \square\% \qquad \frac{1}{50} = 0.0\square = \square\%$$

/5

12–14. This sequence adds the same amount each time. Write the missing numbers.

3   □   □   □   19

/3

List the common factors for each of these.

15. Common factors of 20 and 48. ➔ _____

16. Common factors of 45 and 30. ➔ _____

17. Common factors of 18 and 54. ➔ _____

/3

18–20. Draw a circle around the HCF for each set above.

/3

21. Robert mixes 3 litres of white paint with every 5 litres of blue paint. He needs 24 litres of paint altogether. How many litres of blue paint will he need? _____

/1

22. Circle the number closest in value to 0.2.   0.02   0.18   0.25   0.3   0.11

/1

23. Six snack bars cost a total of £4.80. What is the cost of ten of these snack bars? _____

/1

24. The missing numbers are all prime numbers less than 20. What are the missing numbers?

□ x □ x □ = 165

/1

25. Circle the two numbers which, when multiplied together, have the answer closest to 70.

8.3   10.3   9.7   6.5

/1

Which of these numbers:

380   562   516

547   485

26. Divide exactly by 4? _____

27. Divide exactly by 6? _____

28. Leave a remainder of 2 when divided by 5? _____

29. Leave a remainder of 2 when divided by 3? _____

/4

30–33. Write the name of each of these shapes from its net.

_____   _____   _____   _____   /4

Here are two sides of a square.

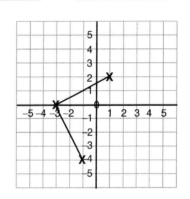

34–36. What are the coordinates of the three vertices?

_____

37. Mark the missing coordinates for the fourth vertex and complete the square.

/4

38–41. Calculate the missing angles. Do not use a protractor.

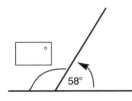 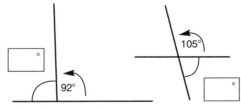 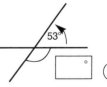

/4

42. Circle two numbers which add up to 1.   0.8   0.03   0.18   0.87   0.92   0.82   /1

43. Use a ruler to draw a pentagon on the grid. The pentagon must have three right angles.

44–45. What are the other two angles of the pentagon? _____

/3

> Circle the best answers for each of these.

46. A post is 4 feet high. Approximately how many metres is this?

  0.4m   1.3m   1.8m   2m   2.2m

/1

47. Approximately how many pints are there in 10 litres?

  8 pints   14 pints   18 pints   22 pints   30 pints

/1

48. This shape is made from equilateral triangles and a square. The square has sides of 15cm. What is the perimeter of the shape? _____

/1

> A bag has 24 beads in it. 7 are black, 8 are dark grey, 4 are white and the rest are light grey.

49. What is the probability of taking out a dark grey bead? _____

50. Another white bead is added to the bag. What is the probability of picking out a white bead now? _____

/2

/50

PAPER 20

1. Tom has £40. He buys three t-shirts at £6.75 each and a jumper costing £18.45. How much money does he have left? _____

/1

2. On the grid draw a triangle with the same area as the rectangle. Use a ruler.

/1

3–5. Write the missing numbers in this sequence.

  ☐   16   25   34   ☐   ☐

/3

6. In a survey of 220 children, 15% of the children asked said that they had gone to bed after 10.00pm the previous evening. How many children in total had gone to bed after 10.00pm?

_____

/1

This is a record of a bus journey.

7. How far did the bus travel between 10.45 and 11.45? _____

8. At approximately what time had the bus travelled 50km? _____

9. How far did the bus travel between 10.30 and 10.45? _____

10. The average speed of the journey was ☐ km/h.

/4

11. A and B each stand for a different number.

A = 6   What is the value of B? _____ A² + A = B + B

/1

12. Circle the offer that sells pens at the lowest individual price for a pen. Use a calculator to help you.

Box of 12 pens: £16.80.	Bag of 6 pens: £9.90.
Offer: Buy 1 box, get 1 box half price	Offer: Buy 2 bags, get 3rd bag free

/1

13–14. Write each set of decimals in order in the boxes to make these correct.

4.73 7.43 3.74 4.47   ☐ < ☐ < ☐ < ☐

29.11 22.3 22.52 29.7   ☐ > ☐ > ☐ > ☐

/2

15–19. Round each amount to the nearest whole number.

29.6cm → _____   9.42ml → _____   £43.39 → _____

27.5g → _____   15.09km → _____

/5

20–23. Complete these equivalent fractions.

$$\frac{2}{5} = \frac{\square}{35} \qquad \frac{15}{21} = \frac{\square}{7} \qquad \frac{3}{\square} = \frac{24}{56} \qquad \frac{7}{10} = \frac{77}{\square}$$

/4

24–27. Draw all of the lines of symmetry on each shape.

/4

28–31. Write the square roots of each of these numbers:

$\sqrt{49}$ = _____ $\sqrt{25}$ = _____ $\sqrt{64}$ = _____ $\sqrt{100}$ = _____   /4

32–35. Write the missing numbers to complete these.

```
    5  6  1 □            5  8  4  8          2  9 □  6          5 □  9  3
+   3 □  5  8        +  3  5  6 □        +  4  6  1 □        +  3  7 □  6
_____        _____        _____        _____

    9  2  7  7          9  4 □  2          6  7  3  2          9  0  8  9
_____        _____        _____        _____
```
/4

36. What is the area of a rectangular building with sides of length 9.5m and 18m? _____   /1

37–42. Draw brackets to make each number sentence true.

19 – 8 – 4 = 7   31 – 9 + 3 = 19   19 – 4 + 8 = 23

18 – 4 + 9 = 5   15 – 9 x 4 = 24   6 + 3 x 8 = 30   /6

43. Circle the two numbers with a difference of 19.   –9   –7   18   8   11   –11   /1

44. The height of a tree is drawn at a scale of 200:1. In the scale drawing,
the height of the tree is 4.8cm. What is the actual height of the tree? _____ metres   /1

45–47. Rectangle ABCD has a diagonal line AC. Calculate the size of angles p, q and r.

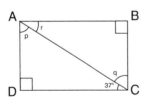

p = _____   q = _____   r = _____   /3

48–50. What is the median for each of the following sets of numbers?

37, 48, 36, 28, 42, 37, 36, 48, 48   Median is _____.

140, 134, 150, 129, 150, 139, 142   Median is _____.

360, 385, 358, 374, 370, 385, 385   Median is _____.   /3

/50

PAPER 21

1–5. What fraction of £10 is:

£2 ☐/☐   £2.50 ☐/☐   £7.50 ☐/☐   50p ☐/☐   £1 ☐/☐   /5

> Write < or > between each pair of amounts.

6. $\frac{5}{6}$ of 30 ☐ $\frac{4}{5}$ of 30   **7.** $\frac{5}{8}$ of 32 ☐ $\frac{3}{4}$ of 32

8. $\frac{2}{3}$ of 60 ☐ $\frac{5}{5}$ of 60   **9.** $\frac{3}{4}$ of 48 ☐ $\frac{5}{6}$ of 48   /5

10. $\frac{6}{7}$ of 28 ☐ $\frac{3}{4}$ of 28

11. Calculate the size of angle x on this isosceles triangle.
Do not use a protractor.

x = _____      /1

12–13. Use a calculator to answer these.

A square has sides of 125mm.
What is the area of the square in square centimetres? _____

A square has an area of 361cm². What is the length of each side? _____   /2

14–15. A 180g snack bar has 60% oats and 40% fruit.

What is the ratio of oats to fruit in a bar, in its simplest form? _____

What is the weight of fruit in the bar? _____   /2

16. Circle the best estimate of 120.38 ÷ 13.14.   5   6   7   8   9   10   11   /1

17. A necklace costs £43 and a ring costs £82. There is a 10% sale
on these items. What will the total cost be in the sale? £ _____   /1

18–20. In these sequences each number is half the previous number. Write the missing numbers.

☐ ☐   56   28   14   ☐ ☐

☐ ☐   88   44   22   ☐ ☐

☐ ☐   152   76   38   ☐ ☐   /3

21–24. Round each amount to the nearest tenth.

/4

8,164 litres → _____   15.86m → _____   9.309 kg → _____   52.949km → _____

25. A sandwich and a sausage roll together cost £3.25. Two sandwiches and a sausage roll together cost £5.45. How much does a sausage roll cost?   £ _____   /1

26. Circle the numbers that are **not** factors of 36.   1   2   3   4   5   6   7   8   9   /1

27–30. Complete these.

```
    9 3 9 4          8 1 0 5          7 7 2 1          6 0 3 4
  + 7 6 5 6        + 3 7 7 3        − 5 3 6 8        − 5 2 9 5
  ─────────        ─────────        ─────────        ─────────


  ─────────        ─────────        ─────────        ─────────
```
        /4

31–32. Calculate the area of these shapes.

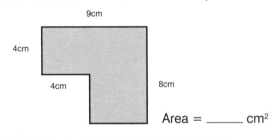

Area = _____ cm²   Area = _____ cm²   /2

> Work out the value of each letter.

33. 8+5y=38   y= _____

34. 4h−15=13   h= _____

35. 29−3v= 2   v= _____

36. 6g+7=55   g= _____   /4

> These ten playing cards are shuffled and placed face down. Write a statement from the list below to show the probability of turning over these cards.

> **Impossible**   **Poor chance**   **Evens**   **Good chance**   **Certain**

37. A multiple of 2 _____

38. A diamond _____

39. A multiple of 5 _____

40. A number greater than 3 _____   /5

41. The queen of diamonds _____

Look at these tile patterns. What proportion of each of the patterns is white?

42.   **43.**   **44.**   **45.**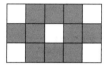

_____ _____ _____ _____

What is the ratio of grey to white tiles in the patterns above?

46. ☐ : ☐   **47.** ☐ : ☐   **48.** ☐ : ☐   **49.** ☐ : ☐   /8

50. A pack of four cakes, including the packaging, weighs a total of 598g.
The packaging weighs 70g. What is the total weight if one of the cakes
is taken out of the pack? _____   /1

/50

PAPER 22

Continue these patterns for two more numbers.

1.   2.31   2.32   2.33   2.34   ☐ ☐

2.   9.059   9.06   9.061   9.062   ☐ ☐

3.   14.75   14.76   14.77   14.78   ☐ ☐   /3

4–9. Write the missing numbers in each of these.

☐ x 10 = 49   6.13 x ☐ = 613   ☐ x 100 = 9377

☐ ÷ 100 = 1.945   9061 ÷ ☐ = 90.61   ☐ ÷ 10 = 37.3   /6

Write the length of time between these pairs of times.

10. | 11.58 | 12.38 | = _____   **11.** | 17.45 | 19.07 | = _____   /4

12. | 06.34 | 10.10 | = ___   **13.** | 08.29 | 9.41 | = _____

Write the numbers 2, 3, 4, 5, 6 or 9 to complete these statements.

14. 280 is a multiple of ☐, ☐ and ☐.

15. 84 is a multiple of ☐, ☐, ☐ and ☐.

16. 432 is a multiple of ☐, ☐, ☐, ☐ and ☐.

17. 4635 is a multiple of ☐, ☐ and ☐.

18. 630 is a multiple of ☐, ☐, ☐, ☐ and ☐.

/5

19–21. Write the missing angle on each of these triangles.

 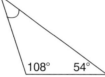 

/3

Write whether these shapes have been **translated**, **rotated** or **reflected**.

22. _____

23. _____

24.  _____

/3

25–27. Calculate the area of these triangles.

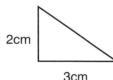 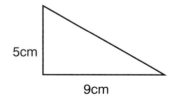

Area of triangle = ___ cm²   Area of triangle = ___ cm²   Area of triangle = ___ cm²

/3

Read and answer these.

28. In a class there are 3 girls to every 4 boys. There are 35 children in the class. How many boys are there? _____

29. The proportion of yellow balloons in a pack is $\frac{3}{7}$. One pack has 15 yellow balloons. How many balloons of all colours are there in total in a pack? _____

30. The proportions of a door are $\frac{2}{5}$ width to height. If the door is 220cm high, what is the width? _____

/3

These pie charts show the results of two football teams. Bilston FC played 36 matches and Farndon FC played 24 matches.

Bilston FC

31. Which team won the most matches? _____

32. How many matches did Bilston FC draw? _____

33. What fraction of their matches did Farndon FC lose? _____

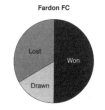

Fardon FC

/3

Calculate the area of these shapes.

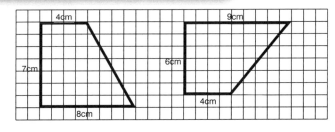

34. Area = _____ cm²   **35.** Area = _____ cm²

/2

36. 180 people went to a school musical. They each paid 95p entrance fee and 90% of them bought programmes for 30p. How much money was paid altogether?

_____

/1

37. Which three prime numbers multiply to make 455?    ☐ x ☐ x ☐ = 455

/1

38. I'm thinking of a number. If I double the number and then subtract 12, the answer is 14. What number am I thinking of? _____

/1

39. Write the missing factors for 54.   ➔(1, ☐) (☐ , ☐) (☐ , ☐) (☐ , ☐)

/1

40.   186
          x 39
       ─────

       ─────

41. 284
      x 17
   ─────

   ─────

42. 365
      x 52
   ─────

   ─────

/3

43–45. Three friends bought some food from a bakery. What is the cost of each item?

| 1 cake
1 sausage roll

Total: £1.85 | 2 cakes
1 sandwich

Total: £2.95 | 1 sandwich
2 sausage rolls

Total: £3.65 |

1 cake = _____   1 sandwich = _____   1 sausage roll = _____   /3

> Tick true or false for each of these statements.

46. Squares are always symmetrical.   True ☐   False ☐

47. All triangles are symmetrical.   True ☐   False ☐

48. Parallelograms have two lines of symmetry.   True ☐   False ☐

49. Semi-circles have only one line of symmetry.   True ☐   False ☐   /4

50. What is the area of a square tile with a perimeter of 36cm? _____   /1

/50

PAPER 23

> Calculate these amounts.

1. 20% of 80cm _____   **2.** 30% of 40km _____

3. 25% of 60kg _____   **4.** 5% of 180ml _____

5. 90% of 50mm _____   **6.** 15% of 140m _____   /6

7–14. Write these numbers on this Venn diagram.

9　5　36　18　22　25　64　15

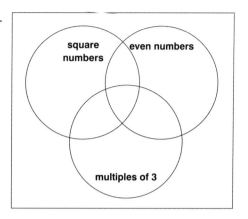

square numbers　　even numbers

multiples of 3

/8

15–17. Join the pairs of prices that total £200.

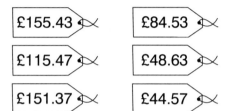

£155.43

£84.53

£115.47

£48.63

£151.37

£44.57

/3

Complete these sentences by writing the most sensible measurement from the list.

18. It takes over an hour to drive _____ to the nearest city.

19. A teaspoon of sugar weighed _____.

20. A bath holds _____ of water.

21. The football pitch in the park is _____ wide.

22. I grew a pumpkin and it weighed _____.

23. My finger is _____ long.

63kg　　6.3g

6.3cm　　6.3kg

63m　　630ml

630 litres　　63km

/6

Write the answer for these.

24. What is 12²? _____

25. What is the next square number after 36? _____

26. What is the square root of 16? _____

27. What is √64? _____

28. What is √1? _____

/5

Calculate the area of these shapes.

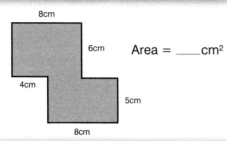

8cm
6cm
4cm
5cm
8cm

Area = ____cm²

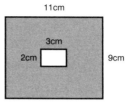

11cm
3cm
2cm
9cm

Area = ____cm²

/2

Write <, > or = to make each statement true.

31. 75% ☐ $\frac{3}{4}$ **32.** 20% ☐ $\frac{1}{2}$ **33.** $\frac{5}{5}$ ☐ 30%

34. 6% ☐ $\frac{1}{6}$ **35.** $\frac{9}{100}$ ☐ 0.9

/5

36. What are the coordinates of triangle A?

(☐ , ☐), (☐ , ☐), (☐ , ☐)

37. Draw triangle B at the following coordinates:
(4,2), (4,5) and (8,5)

38. Is triangle B a translation, rotation or reflection
of triangle A? _____

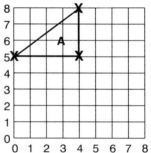

/3

Write the name of each of these shapes from its net.

39. 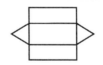   **40.**   **41.**

_____   _____   _____

/3

Write the missing angle for each of these.

42.
78°

43.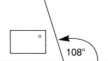
108°

44.
36°

45.
48°

/4

46–48. What are the common factors of these sets of numbers:

18, 42 and 48 → _____   27, 36 and 45 → _____   30, 60 and 90 → _____

/3

49. A pie needs to cook for 50 minutes. It was put in
the oven at 19.38. What time must it come out of the oven? _____ /1

50. Callum buys some ice-creams and some lollies. Ice-creams cost 80p each and lollies
cost 55p each. He buys two more ice-creams than lollies and spends exactly £7.
How many of each does he buy?

_____ ice-creams   _____ lollies /1

/50

TEST 24

Write the missing numbers in each of these.

1. ☐ x 10 = 37   **2.** 9.23 x ☐ = 923   **3.** ☐ x 100 = 8607

4. ☐ ÷ 10 = 15.81   **5.** ☐ ÷ 100 = 3.976   **6.** 9864 ÷ ☐ = 98.64 /6

Write the next two numbers in these sequences.

7. (44)   (29)   (14)   _____   _____

8. ⟨-17⟩   ⟨-11⟩   ⟨-5⟩   _____   _____

9. [-14]   [-5]   [4]   _____   _____

10. ⟨31⟩   ⟨18⟩   ⟨5⟩   _____   _____   /4

11. A plane takes off at 18.27 and takes 3 hours and 46 minutes to reach its destination.
What time will the plane land? _____   /1

12. Shade more squares to make a reflection on the
mirror line.

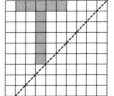

/1

Rearrange each set of digits to make the number nearest to 1.

13. (9) (1) (0) (3)   _____ . _____ _____ _____

14. (2) (0) (1) (8)   _____ . _____ _____ _____

15. (0) (2) (3) (9)   _____ . _____ _____ _____   /3

16. Write the largest whole number to make this true. 60 + ☐ < 93 _____   /1

What is the angle marked *x* in each shape?

17.
angle *x* =

_____

18.
angle *x* =

_____

19.
angle *x* =

_____

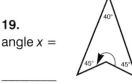

/3

20. A sequence starts at 520 and 90 is subtracted each time.

520   430   340

Write the first two numbers in the sequence which are less than zero. _____ _____   /1

21–23. What are the lowest common multiples of the following:

6 and 8 _____   9 and 4 _____   3 and 5 _____   /3

24. Look at this equilateral triangle inside a rectangle.

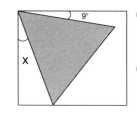

Calculate the value of *x* without using a protractor. _____   /1

25. Write these fractions in order, starting with the smallest.

$\frac{3}{5}$ $\frac{13}{20}$ $\frac{1}{4}$ $\frac{7}{10}$ $\frac{3}{4}$ _____ _____ _____ _____ _____   /1

26. The distance from X to Z is three times as far as from Y to Z. The distance from X to Z is 120cm. What is the distance from X to Y? _____   /1

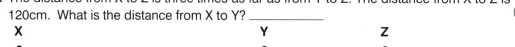

27. Which two factors of 36 add to make 21? _____   /1

28–31. Write the missing digits in these.   415 x 1☐ = 6☐40   7☐ x 39 = ☐886   /4

32–33. Write the missing numbers.   20% of 80 is ☐   20% of ☐ is 80   /2

34. What are coordinates for the vertex A?

_____

35. Draw the two diagonals on the parallelogram.

What are the coordinates for the point where the diagonals cross?

_____

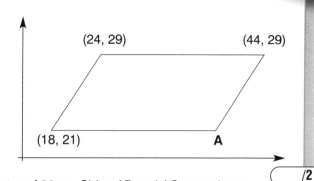

/2

36. Triangle ABC is isoceles and has a perimeter of 30cm. Sides AB and AC are twice as long as BC. What is the length of BC? Do not use a ruler. _____

/1

37. A box contains 2.4kg of rabbit food. How many days would the box of food last if 80g of food was used each day? _____

/1

This scale measures in grams and ounces.

38. Approximately how many ounces is 300 grams? _____

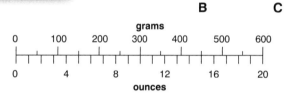

39. Approximately how many grams is 16 ounces? _____

/2

40. A cuboid has a square base of 8cm. The volume of the cuboid is 768cm³. What is the height of the cuboid? _____

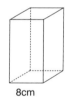

/1

41–46. All of the children at a school choose to have a packed lunch or school dinner. There are 158 children in the school. 29 girls bring a packed lunch. Use this information to complete this table.

	Packed lunch	School dinner	Total
Boys	42		
Girls			86
Total			158

/6

47. A pack of six drinks cartons has 2.07 litres of drink in total. An individual can holds 330ml. Which holds more, a can or a carton? _____

/1

48–50. Find the value of the following expressions if x = 18.

$(43 - x) + 24 = \boxed{}$ $4x - (45 - 16) = \boxed{}$ $(42 - 2x) + 38 = \boxed{}$

/3

/50

anticlockwise	turning in this direction
approximate	a 'rough' answer – near to the real answer
area	the area of a shape is the amount of surface that it covers
axis	(plural is axes) the horizontal and vertical lines on a graph
clockwise	turning in this direction
denominator	bottom number of a fraction, the number of parts it is divided into. Example: $\frac{2}{3}$
difference	the difference between two numbers is the amount that one number is greater than the other. The difference between 18 and 21 is 3
digits	there are 10 digits **0 1 2 3 4 5 6 7 8** and **9** that make all the numbers we use
divisor	a divisor is a number that another number is divided by. For $32 \div 4 = 8$ the divisor is 4
edge	where two faces of a solid shape meet
equation	where symbols or letters are used instead of numbers. Example: $3y = 12$, so $y = 4$
equivalent	two numbers or measures are equivalent if they are the same or equal
equivalent fractions	these are equal fractions. Example: $\frac{1}{2} = \frac{2}{4} = \frac{3}{6}$
estimate	is like a good guess
even chance	if an event has an even chance, there is the same chance of it happening as not happening
faces	the flat sides of a solid shape
factor	a number that will divide exactly into other numbers. Example: 5 is a factor of 20
formula	a formula (plural is formulae) uses letters or words to give a rule
frequency	the number of times that something happens is called the frequency
horizontal	a horizontal line is a straight level line across, in the same direction as the horizon
mean	this is the total divided by the number of items. So the mean of 3, 1, 6 and 2 is $(3 + 1 + 6 + 2) \div 4 = 3$
median	the middle number in an ordered list. Example: 3, 8, 11, 15, 16. The median number is 11

mode	the most common number in a list. Example: 2, 6, 4, 2, 5, 5, 2. The mode is 2
multiples	a multiple is a number made by multiplying together two other numbers
negative number	a number less than zero on the number line
net	the net of a 3D shape is what it looks like when it is opened out flat
numerator	is the top number of a fraction. Example: $\frac{3}{5}$
parallel	lines that are parallel never meet
percentage	this is a fraction out of 100, shown with a % sign
perpendicular	a perpendicular line is one that is at right angles to another line
polygon	any straight sided flat shape
prime factor	any factor that is a prime number is a prime factor. Example: 2 is a prime factor of 10
prime number	only has two factors, 1 and itself. For example, 23 is a prime number as it can only be divided exactly by 1 and 23
proportion	this is the same as finding the fraction of the whole amount. Example: the proportion of black cubes is 3 out of 5 or $\frac{3}{5}$
protractor	a tool for measuring angles
quotient	this is the number of times that one number will divide into another number. Example: When you divide 18 by 3, the quotient is 6
ratio	This compares one amount with another. Example: the ratio of red cubes to blue cubes is 3:2
remainder	if a number cannot be divided exactly by another number, then there is a whole number answer with an amount left over, called a remainder
sequence	a list of numbers which usually have a pattern. They are often numbers written in order
square number	numbers multiplied by themselves make square numbers Example: 4 x 4 = 16. The first five square numbers are 1, 4, 9, 16 and 25
square root	the opposite of a square number. A number, when multiplied by itself, makes a square number. Example: square root of 25 is 5
symmetrical	when two halves of a shape or pattern are identical
vertical	a line that is straight up or down, at right angles to a horizontal line
vertices	(single – vertex) These are the corners of 3D shapes, where edges meet

Progress grid

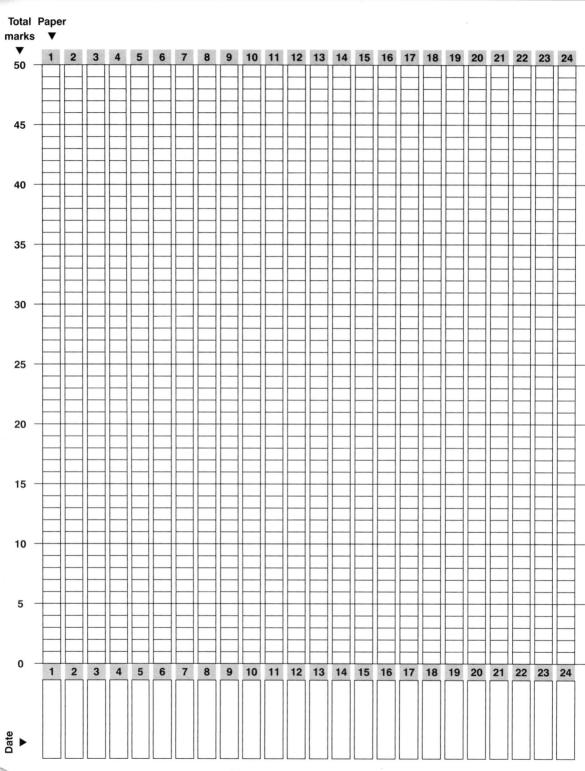

Total Paper
marks ▼
▼

Total marks axis: 50, 45, 40, 35, 30, 25, 20, 15, 10, 5, 0

Paper columns: 1 2 3 4 5 6 7 8 9 10 11 12 13 14 15 16 17 18 19 20 21 22 23 24

Date ▶

Now colour in your score!